HERO

THE INCREDIBLE TRUE STORY OF COURAGE UNDER FIRE

Johnson Beharry, VC
with Jim Eldridge

Scholastic Children's Books
Euston House, 24 Eversholt Street,
London, NW1 1DB, UK

A division of Scholastic Ltd
London ~ New York ~ Toronto ~ Sydney ~ Auckland
Mexico City ~ New Delhi ~ Hong Kong

Published in the UK by Scholastic Ltd, 2014

Text copyright © Johnson Beharry, 2014
Written by Jim Eldridge – with thanks to Nick Cook
Map illustrations by Andrew Pinder, © Scholastic UK

ISBN 978 1407 14679 9

Printed and bound by CPI Group (UK) Ltd, Croydon, CR0 4YY

2 4 6 8 10 9 7 5 3 1

The right of Johnson Beharry to be identified as the author of
this work has been asserted by him in accordance with the
Copyright, Designs and Patents Act, 1988.

INTRODUCTION

The Victoria Cross is the highest medal awarded to British and Commonwealth armed forces. I was proud to be awarded it in 2005, but I was not the first soldier born outside Britain to receive it. In fact, more soldiers born outside Britain have been awarded the Victoria Cross than those born in the United Kingdom. There is a long tradition of soldiers from abroad, mostly from Commonwealth countries, serving with distinction in the British Army.

Those awarded the Victoria Cross have come from Australia, New Zealand, Canada, India, South Africa, Nepal, Fiji, Jamaica, Denmark, Kenya, Sri Lanka, Sweden, Switzerland, Ukraine, and my own home country of Grenada, as well as the British Isles. The British Army is truly a place of many nations serving together.

Johnson Beharry VC

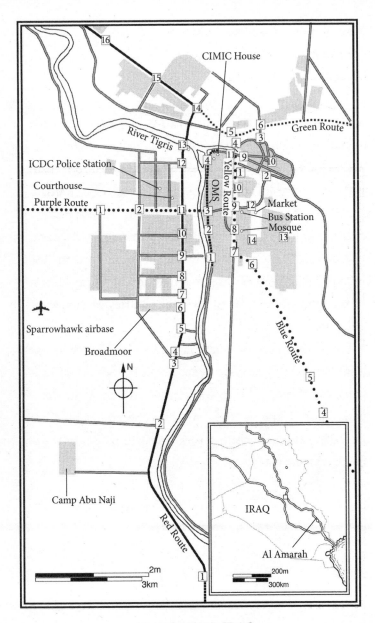

AL AMARAH, IRAQ

Most of what takes place in my story happens either in Iraq or my home country of Grenada – two very different places, but central to everything that has happened to me.

At the back of the book, you'll also find a glossary of some military terms or Grenadian words that might be useful.

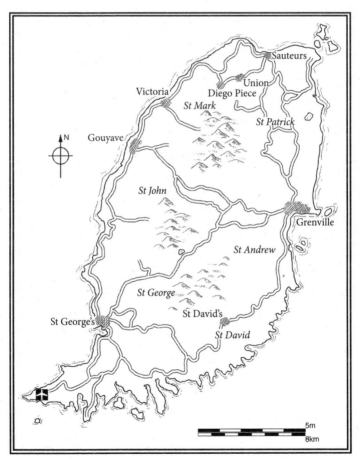

GRENADA

PROLOGUE

Al Amarah, Iraq, April 2004

I check the mirrors of my Warrior armoured vehicle, Whisky Two Zero, and wrench the steering column hard over, putting it into a neutral turn. We send up a shower of sand and grit. The road we've just come down stretches into the distance. I floor the accelerator and watch our speed build. We're on a fast main road and traffic is light, but I need to keep a sharp lookout. There are pedestrians everywhere. Some stop by the edge of the road and stare at us as we roar by. Others carry on as normal as twenty-five tonnes of Warrior hurtles past them. I see kids wobbling on bicycles and old men on donkeys.

As I pass the work party by the street lamp, a couple of them wave. I stick my hand out of the hatch and wave back. The contact area is a small town several kilometres to the southeast of Al Amarah. The road we're on will take us straight to it.

'OK, listen up,' the Light Infantry officer says. 'A platoon operating in convoy with an Iraqi Civil Defence Corps –

ICDC – patrol has been ambushed.'

The army platoon has managed to get out from the contact area, along with one of the ICDC Land Rovers, but this has been hit by small-arms fire, injuring two of its occupants. The other ICDC vehicle is cut off in the town and still under attack. The British Army platoon can't loop back to try to re-establish contact – every time they've tried, they've been attacked by mortars. They need a Warrior to go in for them.

A cluster of buildings – mainly single-storey – rises up on either side of the main road as we approach the contact area. I can see splashes of blue and green – clothes hanging on a line at the back of one of the houses. The officer orders me to pull up on the side of the road while he assesses the situation.

As I pull the Warrior onto the scrub, we hear over the radio that the army patrol has headed back to Abu Naji camp with their casualties. But the ICDC Land Rover is still missing.

'What now, Boss?' I say.

'I'm scanning the town now,' the commander says.

The sunlight is blindingly bright. The only movement I can see is a dog picking its way through a rubbish tip between us and the town. Then I turn and see a group of children running towards us. They're dressed in Arab clothing – long shirts down past their knees – and are waving and shouting.

'Kids to our nine o'clock,' I say.

'That's all we need!' groans the officer.

The kids reach the vehicle. There are four of them, no older than six or seven. They have no shoes on their feet and they're holding their hands out to me. 'They're shoutin' "bakshi" – somet'ing like that,' I say.

'Baksheesh,' Jimmy says. 'It means money. Don't give 'em any.'

I look at the boy nearest to the vehicle. He is jumping up, trying to touch me. His face is filthy and he looks painfully thin, but he is grinning and seems happy enough. I reach into my pocket. I don't have money, but I do have a packet of chewing gum. I hand it to him and he runs off across the sand, chased by his mates.

'OK,' the commander says. 'There's still no contact with the ICDC Land Rover, so we're going to go in and see what we can see. Keep your eyes peeled.'

As I ease Whisky Two Zero forward, Jimmy starts going on about the hatch being open. I don't really see the problem. I prefer to drive with my head out anyway. It's better than hunkering down and using the day sight. But Jimmy doesn't like it at all.

We continue to move forward and then, as we close on the first group of houses, I reduce our speed. Everything is quiet. It's a ghost town. At a crossroads the boss suddenly commands me to reverse up. He's seen something off to our right. I come back and draw level with the crossroads. I glance right and see it too: a vehicle making tracks away from us. I squint against the glare. It's the Land Rover we're looking for. The boss confirms it a second later.

'OK,' he says. 'Looks like they're safe and on their way back to Abu Naji. Might as well follow them, Beharry. Let's get out of here.'

I'm about to slip into drive when Jimmy yells, 'There's a bloke with a rocket-propelled grenade at two o'clock!'

I turn to my two o'clock. There's a man down on one knee in the shadow of a wall. He's so close I can make out the check on his blue and white headgear and see the holes in his faded green combat jacket. And there's something on his shoulder: a black and brown tube, with a brown handle and grip: an RPG.

'Go, go, go!' the boss roars.

'Shut the hatch!' Jimmy shouts.

There's a puff of black smoke and the RPG launcher kicks upwards as the round leaves the tube. Less than a second has passed since the boss ordered me to move, but we're still not going anywhere. I'm frozen – I can't take my eyes off the rocket-propelled grenade that's coming towards us. I can see the cone-shaped warhead and the four little fins that keep it stable. I can see it rotating as it heads straight for us.

'Move!' the boss yells.

The RPG crashes into the armour plating to my left. My

whole world stops. I know what these things can do. I'm waiting for the blast, the shockwave, the blinding, searing heat … Instead I hear a sound like a brick hitting a dustbin lid. The grenade bounces off the hull, then, almost in slow motion, down on to the ground. I watch it roll away, like a drink can some kid just kicked across the street.

I don't hang around to see what happens next. Flooring the pedal, I turn after the Land Rover and keep on going.

Fifteen minutes later we're back at Abu Naji. Jimmy is still shaking when he climbs down from the turret. Unlike Jimmy, I can't get excited about what has just happened to us. It didn't feel real, and still doesn't. I keep on seeing the RPG rolling along the road beside us. Maybe tomorrow they'll go back to throwing stones.

Later, as I'm sitting on the edge of my bed, Sammy and Campbell walk in. They went out on patrol, they saw the town, nothing happened. They ask me about my day. I tell them about my own little adventure.

'What you t'ink happened?' Sammy asks. 'Why did the RPG bounce off the hatch and roll like that?'

'It was a dud,' I tell him.

'There you go,' Sammy says. 'Lucky again.'

'Lucky?' I say. 'We've been mortared, the boss has been fired at – twice – and I get to stare down the barrel of an RPG launcher.'

'You wanted to be shot at and now you have been,' he says.

I suppose he's right.

The next afternoon most of C Company gathers in the tank park for a demonstration by the Light Infantry of how to make a house arrest. It's even hotter than usual outside. Sammy is standing next to me, fanning away the flies as we wait for the demo to begin. I can think of a lot of things I'd rather be doing, but I tell myself that it beats sandbagging, which is what we do when we're not on the road.

A Land Rover pulls up and an officer jumps out. He runs over and pulls Major Coote, Mr Deane and a number of other officers out of the briefing. They move into the shade of a tank and listen to what the officer has to say. I can tell by the look on their faces that it's not good. A moment later they break up the demo and the officer jumps up on to the front of a Warrior. He yells at us to listen up.

'There's a major contact going down right now in the centre of Al Amarah.' He cups his hands around his mouth so we can hear over the noise of a landing helicopter. 'It's serious and it's all happening at Yellow Three. A patrol got hit by a blast bomb as it drove past the Office of the Martyr Sadr, the OMS building.' The OMS building is the HQ of the Mahdi Army, the enemy. 'We have reports of a Land Rover being disabled and several casualties. The platoon is pinned down on the far side of the bridge at Yellow Three by sustained small-arms and RPG fire. Three further platoons have gone into the area to try to assist in an extraction and now they're bogged down as well. One of them was a Land Rover group led by the CO of the Princesses of Wales' Royal Regiment, another by the CO of the Argyll and Sutherland Highlanders.'

Sammy and I look at each other. The centre of Al Amarah is at least fifteen minutes from the camp. Three, maybe four platoons are under attack, big time. And they include the CO, Colonel Maer.

I sprint to the tent, grab my helmet, webbing and SA80 rifle and run back to the tank park. I jump up on to the hull of Whisky Two Zero and drop into the driver's seat. Mr Deane slides into the turret alongside a second lieutenant called Flanagan who is acting as our gunner. A couple of soldiers jump in the back – Big Erv and another man. As I fire up the engine, Mr Deane's voice crackles on the net.

'Bee,' he says, 'you're going to have to pump the gas, mate. The old man needs our help. Get us there as quick as you can.'

'Roger, Boss.'

I release the handbrake, slip into drive and head for the gate. Chris Broome, who we call Broomstick, in his vehicle, Whisky Two Two, is right behind me. In my mirror I see a line of other Warriors kicking up a dust trail behind him. The whole company is heading downtown. I turn left out of the gate on to Red Route, heading for Yellow Three.

As soon as I hit the tarmac, I stand on the accelerator and

get Whisky Two Zero up to her max road speed. Houses dot the scrubland either side of us. A camel nibbles at a dead bush in a dried-up ditch. Electricity lines criss-cross the sky and disappear into the heat haze. We reach the junction where the road splits: Purple Route heading northwest around the perimeter of the city; Red Route running north, parallel to the river. Buildings start to loom out of the haze.

'Hello, Whisky Two Zero, this is Zero,' the Ops Room fires up. 'What's your position?'

There's a faint crackle as Mr Deane switches to the battle-group frequency.

'Whisky Two Zero. At Red Four now.'

To our right I see a group of rusty gantries and cranes, and beyond it, sparkling in the sunshine, the slow-moving surface of the River Tigris. So far there has been very little traffic on the road and I've been able to maintain a steady eighty kilometres per hour. Normally I'm able to take it a little higher. The heat always affects engine performance, but I'm worried about the power pack and make a mental note to check it later.

I look for the street lamp blown up by the roadside bomb – the point we reached yesterday – but it has gone. Ahead, as far as I can see, left and right, are alleyways and houses.

'Kadim Al-Mu'allimin,' Flanagan says. 'Better batten down the hatches.'

'Why?' Mr Deane asks.

'We're about to enter bandit territory,' he replies.

As we pass a cluster of large, rusting tanks, the nerve-ends tighten in my belly. I shift closer to the day sight. I can make out the water tower that Jimmy told me about, at the far end of the boulevard. A column of thick, black smoke rises high into the air beside it.

'Somet'ing's burning pretty bad,' I tell Mr Deane.

'Yeah, I see it,' he says.

Inside the Warrior I'm hotter than I've ever been in my life. Its sides seem to be closing in on me. Pretty soon I won't have room to breathe. I hate driving with the hatch down, but orders are orders, and when I look at the houses either side of the road, I see just how close they are, how easy it would be for someone to shoot us as we go past.

'Whisky Two Zero passing Red Nine,' Mr Deane says.

In the day sight, the column of smoke starts to fill my field of view.

'Bee,' Mr Deane says, 'Lieutenant Flanagan is taking over from here. He knows the ropes. Is that understood?'

'Understood,' I tell him.

'You been downtown before, Beharry?' Flanagan asks.

'No,' I tell him. 'It's me first trip.'

'OK,' he says. 'In around four hundred metres we're going to hit the junction at Red Eleven, right by the water tower. You're going to take a right, which will line us up for the bridge. As you come over the river, you'll see a two-storey building on your left with a mosque next to it. That's the OMS building. We're going to take a slip road off the bridge, loop back under it and take up position in an area of open ground out the front. There are houses and alleyways leading off to the south and west – and somewhere, in among them all, are the trapped call signs. Our job is to extract as many men as we can and head back to Abu Naji. Is that clear?'

'Yes, sir.'

'Good lad.'

As we draw closer to the junction at Red Eleven, you'd never know there was a major gun battle going on. A woman dressed in black makes her way down an alleyway to our right, struggling to hang on to two plastic bags full of shopping. A man carrying a door on his head stops and stares at us as we rumble past. A group of children watch us from a crumbling balcony. One of them is sucking a lollipop. All we can hear is the growl of our diesel engine and the clank and squeak of tracks.

I think back to what Mr Deane once said about situational awareness; how, as an infantryman with a distrust of vehicles, he hates to feel cooped up inside a Warrior. This must be doing his head in.

Electricity wires criss-cross the street like spider's webs. As we approach downtown, the city looks a complete mess. The water tower casts a shadow across the street. We've reached the junction at Red Eleven. I check for traffic, but there are no cars anywhere, so I turn right and ease Whisky Two Zero on to Purple Route. Ahead, just beyond the river, thick, black smoke billows up from under the bridge.

'Keep going,' Flanagan says, 'keep going …'

As we rumble over the river, I check my mirror. Whisky Two Two, Broomstick's wagon, pulls on to Purple Route behind me.

'There's a slip road on the right,' Flanagan says. 'You should see it any moment.'

I peer through the day sight. Smoke drifts across the bridge.

'Trust me, it's coming up,' Flanagan says.

I'm about to flick the day sight to passive night vision, so I can see through the smoke, but a breeze blows up from the river and the ramp suddenly appears. I turn off the bridge, on to the slip road. We loop down and around to the right, coming back under the bridge, which carries on as a flyover into the east side of town. A Snatch Land Rover with a jagged hole in its right side is burning out of control on the central reservation ahead of us. Beyond the Land Rover, to the left, is the mosque, and what I take to be the OMS building.

I move forward to allow the vehicles behind me to roll on to the area of open ground in front of them. The CO comes over the radio. He is down to two Land Rovers. The third has managed to get away from the area, taking a casualty to Abu Naji.

I'm concentrating too hard on my surroundings to pay much attention to what is being said. All I catch is the fact that there's enemy in the OMS building, enemy in the mosque and enemy in the alleyways that feed into the square. I hear the CO telling us to engage the OMS building. Seconds later Flanagan opens up with our chain gun. I watch a line of bullets hammer the front of the building and flashes of tracer punching through windows and hitting the interior walls.

'Enemy two o'clock to turret!' Mr Deane shouts.

I see bursts of fire from an alleyway; hear the rattle of our chain gun. I watch a line of bullets snake along the ground and bounce off the walls. A man wearing blue jeans, a white T-shirt and a cloth wrapped around his head appears out of the shadows.

Oh, God, a civilian, I say to myself. But at that moment, almost as if he's heard me speak, he stops and turns our way. I see a face, twisted by hatred. I also see that he's carrying a rifle, an AK47…

'Gunman, Boss, moving left to right, three o'clock to vehicle.'

'I can't see a thing!' Mr Deane shouts.

The gunman darts back through the doorway of a house. From the two windows on the floor above I notice little bursts of light and hear what sounds like stones pinging off our armour.

'There's enemy in that house, second floor, three o'clock to vehicle! They're firing at us!' I yell.

I hear the whir of the turret as it rotates, the *ratatatatat* of the chain gun. The wall below one of the windows disintegrates in a cloud of dust. Two Warriors shoot past. Out of the corner of my eye I see one take up position at the top of an alleyway. Its turret trains on the OMS building and a line of tracer pours in through a window on the ground floor.

I catch movement off to our right and turn to see two men pushing a white Datsun saloon into the square. A head and shoulders bob up behind one of the windows and I get a glimpse of a black and brown tube...

'RPG! Behind the white car, two o'clock to vehicle!'

The figure behind the car stands up, steadies the tube on the boot and fires. The RPG roars away from the launcher, trailing a ribbon of smoke. It disappears beyond the field of view of my day sight.

Flanagan opens up and I see bullets punch into the side of the Datsun. The rear window shatters and the two people pushing it flee into an alley. I see no sign of the guy with the RPG. I turn the steering column to the left and we neutral-turn a fraction, enough for me to see where the RPG ended up.

There's a smoking hole in the wall of a house on the corner of an alleyway opposite the OMS building. In front of it is another wall running at waist height, parallel with the alley. I spot movement through the smoke between them. I flick to passive night vision as a figure in a camouflage shirt pops up from behind the wall, fires his rifle and ducks back down again. He is followed a second later by another guy, who lets off a burst in the same direction.

'Boss, I can see our guys,' I yell over the radio. 'To our ten o'clock.'

Flanagan is still firing in the direction of the OMS building.

'Got 'em,' Mr Deane says.

'What do you want me to do?' I ask.

'Reverse up. Get our back end tight against that wall, so they're shielded as they get in. Think you can manage that?'

'No problem,' I tell him. I angle the nose around to the right, until the RPG hole in the side of the building slides into view in my mirror. Then I slip the vehicle into reverse.

Mr Deane talks to Broomstick in Whisky Two Two. Both wagons are going to go in and pick up the dismounts. Bullets crack against the armour somewhere above my hatch. I slam on the brakes and we rock to a halt a few metres from the wall outside the house where the dismounts are holed up. Behind me, I can hear the crack of our chain gun again and, through my headset, Mr Deane still cursing his head off because he can't see a damn thing.

Right on the edge of the day sight's field of view, I see Whisky Two Two slide into position beside us.

'Forget this for a game of soldiers!' Mr Deane snaps. 'I'm

opening the hatch.'

If it's OK now for Mr Deane to open his hatch, I figure it's OK for me to.

I stick my head out just in time to see Broomstick jumping off the turret of Whisky Two Two. The two Warriors are just a few feet apart. Bullets ping and ricochet off Broomstick's wagon. Whisky Two Two's rear door is already open.

Soldiers start to roll over the wall and jump into the back. Mr Deane fires his SA80 at the OMS building and I hear his bullets fly over my head. I glance back.

Chris Broome is yelling, 'Move, move, move …!'

Soldiers continue to jump over the wall and pile into the back of our two wagons. By now the enemy have got our range and bullets are flying off our armour. Broomstick is standing in the gap between the two vehicles, still shouting at the dismounts from the Rover group to get a move on. He ducks and curses as bullets fly past his head.

Mr Deane and Flanagan are still hosing down the OMS building.

'Is everybody in?' Mr Deane shouts.

'Yeah,' Broomstick yells back. 'Both wagons are packed out. You've got thirteen in the back of yours, including the CO from the Argylls.'

'What about the rest?'

'They're breaking out with the CO in the two remaining Snatches from his Rover group.'

'Then we're outta here,' Mr Deane says.

'Boss, the door's still open,' a voice announces in my headset.

'Who's that?' Mr Deane says.

'Erv, Boss.'

'Then shut it!'

'There's too many people back here. We can't shut the door!'

Broomstick is crouched between the vehicles.

'Chris?' Mr Deane shouts. 'Our door won't shut. Can you close it from the outside?'

Broomstick runs around the back. I can hear shouting over Erv's radio; people are getting squashed.

Broomstick reappears and gives Mr Deane a thumbs-up. The rear door is shut. We're good to go. The trouble is, there's not enough room in the back of Whisky Two Two for Broomstick. I'm wondering what the hell's going to happen, when a Snatch drives past.

Broomstick sees it too. He leaps out and flags it down. The Land Rover screeches to a stop. Broomstick jumps in the back and they take off, heading for the bridge.

'Beharry, go, go, go! ' Flanagan shouts. 'Don't let that Snatch out of your sight.'

I hit the accelerator. A Warrior is meant to take a maximum of seven people in the back. We have thirteen. They must be crammed to the roof in there.

I hear a lot more swearing and shouting over Erv's radio. We drive up the ramp, back on to the bridge and take a left on to Red Route by the water tower. Two hundred metres down the road, a gunman springs out of an alleyway and fires as we drive past. It's only when one of his bullets cracks off the turret and whistles past my ear that I realize I'm driving through bandit country with the hatch open. Too late to close it now.

I step on the accelerator and watch the needle on the speedometer. I can barely reach forty-five. All I can see is houses stretching into the distance. This time, though, there's nobody on the street and no kids staring down at us from balconies. Erv comes on the radio again; he sounds like someone is strangling him.

'Boss, it's hard to breathe back here. Can we stop so some of us can get out?'

'No,' Mr Deane says. 'We're still being shot at.'

'It's not me who's asking, Boss.'

'Who is?' Mr Deane asks.

'The CO of the Argylls – Lieutenant Colonel Grey.'

There's a pause. Then Mr Deane says, 'Perhaps you could politely inform the colonel, in the interests of his own safety, that he's going to have to grin and bear it till we're out of the contact area.'

Fifteen minutes later we pull up just inside the main gates at Sparrowhawk. The back of Whisky Two Zero is like a furnace and Big Erv is worried that some of the dismounts are going to die unless we pull over and give them some air and water.

After everyone has piled out I see Colonel Grey take Mr Deane to one side. The CO of the Argylls is bathed in sweat. His face is pale and for a moment I think he wants to punch somebody. I can't hear the conversation, but by the time Mr Deane finishes talking with him, Colonel Grey's face softens and they end up shaking hands. Fifteen minutes later, after we have all drunk some water and cooled down a bit, we pile back into the Warrior and head back to Abu Naji.

Back at camp the twenty-odd soldiers we extracted from Yellow Three gather around our vehicles to chat excitedly about the battle. Radio reports confirm that no one was killed, but we do have casualties, at least three, the most serious being Lance Corporal Kev Phillips, who's had a bullet hit his shoulder blade, then exit through the side of his neck. He's on his way to the field hospital at Shaiba and is expected to make a full recovery.

An officer appears and gets the men to ensure that their weapons are all clear of ammunition; the last thing anyone wants at this stage is a man killed by a negligent discharge. As the dismounts head off towards the accommodation area to shower, change and eat, I can hear them whooping and high-fiving until they disappear around the side of a building.

'Bee?'

I turn. Mr Deane is climbing out of the turret. He has sweat and dust all over his face and he looks like he's lost a few pounds since the last time I saw him.

'You OK?' he asks.

'Yes,' I tell him, 'I'm fine.'

It's easier than saying I don't know what I feel. 'Exhausted' comes close. 'Drained' comes closer. But neither fully describes my emotions after what just happened.

'You did brilliantly, son,' Mr Deane says. 'Your driving was outstanding.'

'Thanks, Boss.'

'I mean it,' he says. 'What you did – manoeuvring the vehicle the way you did – took a lot of skill.'

'What I did weren't no different from the way Malloy drove,' I say.

Malloy is Broomstick's driver.

'Yeah, well,' he says. 'I'm proud of you both.' He wipes the sweat off his forehead with the back of his hand and hops down to the ground. 'Why don't you go grab a shower and a cup of tea? You've earned them.'

'If it's all the same, Boss, I'm going to stay with the wagon. I want to make sure she's cleaned up and ready to roll for the next time. There's somet'ing not quite right with the power pack. I need to take a look at her ...'

'I can send someone over to help you,' he cuts in, glancing at the sky. It's six o'clock, a couple of hours from sunset, but the heat is still unbelievable.

'That's all right, Boss. I'm OK. I rather be on me own.'

'Well, don't overdo it, eh?' he says.

I hop down on to the ground and start to walk around the vehicle. There are chips and nicks everywhere. I give up counting how many bullets must have struck us. The good thing is none of them has done us any damage. When I get to the back of the vehicle I see that a light cluster is missing. I think it must have been hit by a stray bullet. But when I check the other one I see that's missing too. Somebody has unscrewed them. I remember the kids we ran into yesterday. Bloody hell, Johnson, I say to myself, while you're handing out gum, some kid's unscrewing your light clusters. I can't help smiling. Not so long ago that kid was me.

CHAPTER 1

My mind goes back to when I am a small boy, growing up as one of a big family in Grenada, an island in the southern Caribbean.

Driving is my big love. The speed, the gear changes, the smell and sound of fast cars.

My dad can't read, but sometimes, when he's not being angry, I sit on his lap, out on the porch as the sun goes down, and we go through the pictures in car magazines together. I get my brother Jude to read out the models' specs. I like Jaguars, Ferraris and Maseratis, but the Porsche 911 Turbo 3.3, the fastest production car in the whole world, is the only one for me.

Our house is tiny, about four metres by four metres, and sits in the middle of a clearing at the top of a hill that's so steep it's like a pillar of rock. Somehow our house contains three little bedrooms – each the same size as the bed in it – and a kitchen. The kitchen is bare but for a stool and a small table where my gran sits when it is raining, and a cupboard where she keeps a few pots.

My grandpa, Cyril Bolah, built the house. Its base is

secured to the rock with metal stakes, but some of them have come loose and, when the wind blows, the whole place creaks and groans like an old ship and moves another few inches towards the edge of the hill. The first time I felt this happen, I ran into my gran's room and jumped into her bed. As she held me close and I listened to the beat of her heart, she told me how we Grenadians are blessed, because God has not sent a hurricane to the island since more than thirty years ago, when Janet swept through.

'They say God is a Grenadian, 'cos all the other islands in the whole Caribbean get hit by hurricanes 'cept us,' she said, stroking my head. 'We Grenadians is special.'

If the house that my grandpa built survived Hurricane Janet, she said, it can survive anything. But to be on the safe side she hummed her favourite hymn, 'Blessed Assurance', and I can hear her humming it now.

Today, from the woods below my gran's house, I hear my mother calling. As I burst through the bushes, my mother is standing on the porch, balancing my little brothers Jade on one hip and Jeffon on the other. My brother and sister, Jeffrey and Jemeela, are both clinging to her skirt. Jemeela is sucking her thumb. Jade is crying. My big brother Jude is there. My older sister Jill is holding a plastic bag full of our clothes. There are no lights on in the house and the shutters are closed.

Some houses in Diego Piece are built on solid foundations

and made entirely of brick. Some are built into the sides of hills and need pillars to support them at the front. Ours is the only house I know that is built entirely on stilts, in a dip where the stream floods when the rains come. When the wind blows and I'm lying in bed at night, I feel it swaying.

My mother looks down at me and I smile, but her expression doesn't alter. I touch her hand and it's cold. It's as if the whole world has suddenly become a different place.

'What's the matter?' I ask. 'Where we goin'? Where's Daddy?'

'We have to leave,' she whispers in a voice that is so faint I can hardly hear the words. 'Jude, take hold of Jade. Jill, go back into the house and make sure the shutters are locked. Johnson, you carry the clothes. Everyone need to help.'

'Where we goin'?' I say again. 'Why isn't Daddy with us?'

'We need to hurry,' my mum says.

'Where's Daddy?' I ask again.

Jude puts a hand over my mouth.

'No more questions,' he says quietly, 'I tell you when we get there.'

'Get where?'

Jill comes out of the house carrying the saucepan full of chicken stew and dumplings. I understand now. There will be no supper around the table tonight.

Jude is first up the path. He lifts Jade and places him on his shoulders. My mother goes next, carrying Jeffon. Jemeela,

Jill, Jeffrey and I follow.

I've been here before on this path, in the darkness: Jude, Jill, Jemeela, Jeffrey, Jeffon, Mummy and me, all of us stealing from our own house in the middle of the night.

I think I hear a noise behind us; someone is following. I turn slowly, but there's nothing there. The only movement is the ripple of the stream. My nan – my mother's mum – and my mum's sister, Aunt Ena, are waiting at my nan's house in the middle of the village. Nobody says a word as they open the door and show us in. The door shuts as quickly as it opens. My mum hands Jeffon to my nan. She sways and for a moment I think she's going to faint. But then she holds the edge of the table and steadies herself. Nan and Ena direct my mum, Jill, Jemeela, Jeffrey and Jeffon up the stairs. I'm about to follow them when Ena stops me.

'There's no more room upstairs, Treasure,' she whispers, 'but I fix a bed for you and Jude out back. You be nice and safe there.' She raises a finger to her lips. 'But you must promise, promise me, to keep quiet.' She opens her eyes wide, pretending it's a game. But whatever this is, I know it's no game. 'Can you keep quiet?' Ena whispers. 'Not a sound?'

'Don't worry,' Jude says. 'He will.'

We step out into the courtyard. I hear my nan pull down the shutters at the front of the house. In the dim light at the back it's difficult to see where I'm going, but Jude seems to know the way. He takes my hand and moments later I find myself under the roof of the lean-to where my nan keeps her goat and rabbits.

The goat bleats as we settle on to the bed of clean straw that my auntie has prepared for us. I hear scuffling sounds from the rabbit hutch. I lie there not saying a word, just listening to the sounds of the village and watching the moon as it crosses the night sky. Dogs bark; I hear the distant sound of a radio. Inside the house, the lights stay off. Nan's home, normally alive with activity, is as quiet as the graveyard at the bottom of the village.

'Jude,' I whisper. 'You awake?'

He grunts. 'Go to sleep, Johnson.'

'I'm not goin' to sleep till you tell me what we doin' here.'

'Sleep,' he says.

I sit up and hit my brother in the ribs. He stifles a cry of pain and says, 'What you doin'? You crazy?'

'I'm goin' to scream and shout and punch the goat so the goat scream and shout too, unless you tell me why we here.'

'Keep your voice down,' Jude hisses.

'Tell me, then.'

'All right. We here 'cos it's Friday.'

'Friday? What's so special about Friday?'

'Friday night is the night Daddy get paid.'

'So? Old Man Baptiste pay Daddy every week. What's so different about this week?'

Jude is five years older than me. He's at senior school in

Sauteurs. He gets A grades in almost everything he does. He's my half-brother, but the fact we have different fathers doesn't make any difference to me.

'I want the truth,' I say. 'Tell me.'

For a long time Jude says nothing. Then he sighs. 'Do you ever t'ink about the house we live in?'

'It's our home. What's there to t'ink about?'

'Our house is only four years old, but the wood is old and rotten. Don't you ever wonder why our house is almost new yet it's fallin' apart?'

I shake my head.

'Do you want to know?' Jude says.

'I t'ink so …'

'You were the one who say you goin' to scream the place down if I don't tell you.'

'OK,' I say, 'I want to know.'

'After Mummy leave school she go to work in the Pool in Victoria – the place where the nutmeg go to be weighed, washed and peeled. She meet my dad, Lexan Williams, but the two of them split when I'm still a baby. Then Mummy meet a guy called Ken. He work at the Pool too. But when Mummy get pregnant with Jackie, Ken go to England – he have relatives there.

'When Jackie is born, Mummy write to Ken for money. But Ken never send her anything, so she go back to the Pool. She get my nan and Ena to look after me and Jackie and she work there all day. She work so hard it make her sick.

'But then she meet Daddy – your Daddy, my … new Daddy – and they take a room in a house down by the school. That's when Mummy she t'ink her life change. Daddy work hard. He work in the day for Old Man Baptiste and after he finish on the plantation he go an' work on a buildin' site, usually for Devlin. Daddy make more than seventy-five dollars a week. Mummy make a bit too. Life was pretty good then.'

'What happen?' I ask.

'One day the owner say he sell the whole house to Mummy and Daddy for five hundred dollars. Mummy and Daddy they save a bit and borrow the rest and soon the house is theirs – a great big house, with four bedrooms.'

I sit up straight.

'Four bedrooms!'

This is the first time anybody tell me this. Four bedrooms. This is as big as any house in the village, except for Old Man Baptiste's and the new one they're building on the corner.

'Shhh!' Jude puts his hand over my mouth. 'Two months later Mummy and Daddy find out that there are all sort o' problem with the house an' from that day they have not'ing.' He waits a while and says, 'That's when he start drinkin'.'

'But everybody in Grenada drink …'

'With Daddy it was different. He always wait till Friday, the day he get paid, and then he go down to the store and he buy a big bottle of rum. And then he sit down and he play cards with the other guys and by the end of the night he lose a whole heap of money. The next night he go back again, drink another bottle and he lose a whole lot more. By Sunday there's not'ing left. This go on for week after week.

'But you know what Mummy do? One weekend she get a whole load of people together and she take that house apart, piece-by-piece. And everyone carry the pieces to the bottom of the hill where Gran lives and they build that house in the only place in the village they can – on Gran's land. A funny little scrap of land at the bottom of the hill that's good for not'ing 'cos the stream turn the whole place into a swamp.'

'But why can't we stay in our own house? Why do we have to stay at Nan's? So what if Daddy get a little drunk?'

Jude sits up. He leans on his elbow and looks at me.

'When Daddy start drinkin' on a Friday night he don't stop till Sunday night. That's why we have no money, Johnson. Daddy drink an' gamble away all the money he ever earn. An' when he drink he get angry – you seen him. Not just vex; he get really angry. That's why we have to move. Someone say they see Daddy comin' up the road with a bottle of rum. When he come home drunk, he hit Mummy. An' now Mummy afraid he goin' to start on us too.'

*

I get up as soon as the stars that I can see through the holes in the lean-to are gone. I've not slept much. The things Jude said can't be true, I keep telling myself. My dad is a quiet man, who works hard. He has never had an easy relationship with Jude, because he is not his real son. So maybe, I tell myself, Jude is making these things up. But I've never known Jude to lie to me before. All I want is to go home and see my daddy – to sit with him out on the porch, the two of us together, and leaf through the pages of my car magazine. If I could just be with him I know everything would be all right.

But Jude has made it clear that none of us is to set foot back in the house until Monday, when Daddy goes back to work again. These are Mummy's rules. When my father starts to drink he doesn't stop until he has to go back to work. Jude told me the last time this happened, when I was three, my mother came back to the house to collect some clothes for Jeffrey and Jeffon, and my dad beat her because she woke him up when she tripped over a crate of beer that was lying on the floor of their bedroom. All we can do is lie low at my nan's until he drinks the house dry. If he passes by, trying to find us, my nan and Ena will send him packing. They're both strong women. And my dad knows that he owes Ena four hundred dollars. Even though he knows we're here, and this will make him angry, he's not likely to come looking for us. By the time Monday comes around he will have forgotten we were ever gone.

That, Jude tells me, is how much my dad drinks. He drinks so much that he has no memory of it. As soon as he has gambled all his money away, by the early hours of Saturday morning, he goes back home to carry on drinking alone. And he keeps going till the last drop.

CHAPTER 2

Next day, I sneak back to our house. I don't tell no one I'm goin' because they'd stop me. I just go. I want to see my dad.

He's there, sitting on the porch in his favourite chair. He's smiling. He looks happy. I don't know what I expected; windows smashed maybe, or the sound of him in a rage somewhere inside the house. But he looks just the same. There's nothing different about him. He's not a monster. He's my dad. Beside him is a small table and on the table are a bottle and glasses. I feel a tingling sensation in my stomach. I'm spying on my father. It feels strange. But I'm excited too. I recognise the bottle. It's clear, with a black and white striped label. Even though I can't read I know that the red writing on the white part says 'Original White Rum'.

My father leans forward and his leg knocks against the table. For a moment he stares as it dances in front of him. Then he lunges, grabbing the bottle by the neck. The table falls and one of the glasses shatters. My father leans over and picks up the table. He tries to set it back on its legs, but it falls over again. I hear him cuss, and he has another go. This time he succeeds. He puts the bottle back, then gets down on his hands and knees and grabs the glass that hasn't broken. He says something to himself, then, as if he's shooing away a fly, he brushes the pieces of glass from the balcony with the back of his hand. Then he holds his hand up and watches blood trickle down his arm. I figure that he'll go into the house and get a piece of cloth and tie it round his hand, but he just flops back into his chair and stares at the sky. I take a step forward. My father is hurt. I want to help him.

A twig breaks. The sound is so soft I hardly hear it myself, but it's enough to set off the dogs. They start to bark and howl from underneath the house. I drop to the ground. I've never liked the dogs. They scare me. We keep them to frighten away thieves.

I think about running away, but I'm afraid my father will see me. I've heard the anger in his voice. I don't know what he will do if he realises I've been spying on him. He makes his way slowly down the steps, the bottle of rum in his hand. Then he drops to his knees and buries his face in his hands.

A peal of thunder rolls up the valley. It starts to rain. The rain is falling hard now. Drops the size of cherry stones hit the ground around me. I want to throw myself in my dad's arms. I want him to hold me, but I turn and run. I run so fast I don't even notice the branch that whips across my head.

At the top of the path I stop and look back. I don't know where my father is now.

I tell myself he's not a bad man. But thoughts I don't want to have twist in and out of my mind.

*

The ground around my gran's place is completely flat, as if a giant has taken a machete and chopped off the top of the hill and hurled it into the sea. The sound of singing reaches me from the other side of the house as I get near. To get to her house I have to dodge around the tiny vegetable patch where my gran grows just about everything she needs – saffron, celery, sweet potato, melons, pumpkins, gungo peas, tomatoes and cabbages – alongside the fruits that grow up here wild. There are carambolas – star-fruit trees – mammy apples, soursops, avocados, mangoes and pawpaws. I like the soursop most, a fruit with a spiny skin that can grow as big as my head. My gran slices off the top with a sharp knife, then gives me the only spoon she has in the house, so I can scoop out the soft flesh. It's the closest thing in the forest to ice cream.

I dart behind the house and check the shower, because sometimes my gran sings when she's scrubbing herself. The shower is a bucket with holes in the bottom that my grandpa rigged up in a tree. Fifteen years after my grandpa built it, it's still here and it still works.

My grandpa died when I was a baby and, though my

gran swears she sees his ghost sometimes, the reality is, she's all alone. At the base of the tree is a barrel that collects rainwater. When my gran wants a shower, she scoops water out of the barrel, climbs a little ladder and slops the water into the bucket. If you fill the bucket to the top you get a shower that lasts about two minutes. It takes several trips to fill the bucket to the top. This is easy for me, because I move with the speed of a cat, but for my gran it's a different story. By the time she fills the bucket with a second scoop, the first has drained away.

The best thing about the shower, I think, is the view. From this side of the house you can see all the way across the sea to Carriacou, the second biggest island in the Grenadines. Today the air is so clear I can see large ships steaming past Carriacou towards St Vincent.

I hear singing again – the first verse of 'Blessed Assurance' – but now it sounds as if it's coming from the front of the house. This is the trouble with the strange, magical place where my gran lives: the wind can whip your words away, swirl them through the branches of the big old trees and throw them back at you from a completely different direction. My gran says that this is the trees making mischief, but I'm too old to believe in those stories any more. When I was little, three or four, I used to come up here and sit on my gran's lap, out the front of the house, where she always sits when the sun goes down. She'd say, 'Johnson, what you wan' to do wit' you life?' And I'd tell her, 'Gran, I want to be a driver.' And she would say, 'What kin' of driver?' And I would say, 'A racin' driver.' And she would say, 'Where you get these ideas from?' And I would say, 'From my dad.' And then she would tell me that when he was little my dad was a dreamer too, just like me, his head filled with all kinds of crazy ideas.

There's a spot just below her house where my gran goes in the morning, often just as the sun is coming up; a piece of ground between her big old cedar tree and the mango, where you can see everything – the whole world – all at once: sea, valley, mountains, trees and sky. I go there now and see her standing with a brush in her hands, sweeping the leaves off the top of my grandpa's grave.

My grandpa is buried in a raised tomb around three feet high, and it gleams white because every year my gran gets one of us – her grandchildren – to give it a fresh lick of whitewash. It's a job that she offers only to her 'fav'rit gran'chillun', but as she has a favourite grandchild from each of her nine children, there are quite a few she can call on to do the job. My gran is very open about which of us are her favourites, but says she can't make up her mind between me and Jill. We're both favourites.

I notice, though – and this warms my heart when I think on it – that Jill doesn't ever get to paint my grandpa's grave.

I love my sister, but she's the one who likes to rule the roost. Most of my brothers and sisters just take it, but not me.

Jill and I argue a lot.

The sight of my gran, and the sound of her voice as she sings, pull me up short. I can hear in the words of the chorus how much she still loves him: 'This is my story, this is my song, Praising my Saviour all the day long. Angels descending bring from above Echoes of mercy, whispers of love . . .' She thinks it describes how Heaven will look when she and my grandpa are together again. I tiptoe away, back towards the house, and climb into the roots of the old cedar tree.

'Johnson?'

Even though she doesn't have a tooth in her head, my gran still manages to beam me a huge, radiant smile. Words can't express just how much I love her in this moment. I struggle to hold back my tears.

My gran comes and sits on the roots.

'Are you goin' to speak to me about it, chile?' she says.

'Speak about what, Gran?'

'Whatever it is that's vexin' you so bad.' She leans forward and touches the skin around the cut on my head. 'An' how you come by this?'

I shrug.

'It's nothing, Gran. Me an' Ansell have a fight, that's all.'

Ansell is an older cousin on my mother's side. My father's family are all of Indian descent; my mother is half-Indian, half-Negro. Ansell is always picking on me. I don't like him at all.

'Do you want to tell me about it?' my gran asks, arching an eyebrow.

'There's not much to tell,' I say, looking down at my feet.

'So how come you mammy not put a poultice on it?'

I see the look on her face and know that she's never going to leave this alone.

'You bes' come along,' she says.

I follow her into the kitchen. My gran walks slowly. She doesn't use a stick, but she probably should; every now and then she has to stop and catch her breath. Jude says she has a bad heart, but when I ask my gran about this she says there is nothing wrong with her; she's just getting old. I've no idea how old she is, but I've never seen anyone with so many lines on their face.

She reaches on top of her cupboard and brings down a small clay pot. Then she leads me back outside and sits me down on the rocks. Her poultice is filled with all kinds of herbs and leaves, and salt and sugar and rum. She scoops three fingers into the pot and starts to apply the brown, sticky paste to the cut. It smells terrible but feels cool and soothing on my skin.

'I ask you one mo' time,' my gran says. 'If you mammy see you yesterday, she'd a treated you sheself.' Again she looks at me. 'So where you were, Johnson?'

'I stay out late,' I tell her. 'I didn't see Mummy since it

happen.' I pause. 'We stayin' by my nan's for a few days.'

I hope she doesn't ask me why. I know that Daddy and my gran don't always get along. In the days when she used to come down the hill and see us, there were times when I saw the two of them argue pretty badly. My gran can be bossy when she wants to be (maybe this is why Jill is also her favourite, because Jill is just like her) and this can make my dad get pretty vex. In our house he wants to be boss. Sometimes my gran goes to church. The rest of the time she stays here, looking after her garden and talking to my grandpa. If she needs anything she calls down and one of us will go get it.

Maybe she doesn't know of my dad's drinking.

'Daddy get sick an' we have to leave the house so he can get better,' I say, choosing my words carefully. I can't bring myself to look at her. I stare at my toes instead. They're covered in little nicks and cuts from the rocks under the bridge.

Luckily my gran's eyesight is too bad to see them, otherwise she'd have covered them in a poultice too.

'When he get sick?'

'Friday,' I say. 'Friday night.'

'An' that's when you leave the house – all of you?'

'Yes,' I tell her.

For a long time my gran says nothing. Sometimes we sit on these steps and watch the seabirds soaring on the breeze.

Sometimes I just sit here alone, watching her cook or pick through her vegetable garden. My happiest moments are when we sit quietly on these rocks, the two of us together. But this is a different kind of silence. When she opens her mouth again, my gran uses a voice I've never heard in her before.

'Johnson, you listen to me now, an' you listen to me good. What are the three most important things in life? What am I always tellin' you?'

'Love, respect, honesty, Gran.'

'Love, respec', honesty,' she repeats. 'The only three things you need in life.' This is what she tells all her grandchildren. They're the very first things I can remember her saying to me. 'An' now I want you to tell me the truth,' she says. 'The absolute truth.'

I raise my eyes to hers. I try to force back the tears, but this time I can't. And with the tears everything else tumbles out too. When I tell her what happened down at the house, what I saw with my own eyes, my gran makes a sudden noise, like something catching in her throat.

'Gran?'

'It's not'ing,' she says. 'Don' pay me no min'.'

She gets to her feet and stares out across the valley. I feel a huge sadness in my heart. I've told her the truth. I've told her what I saw. But from the look I've just seen pass across her face, I know I've done a terrible thing. What will she do?

Is she going to cuss me for saying these things? Is she going to tell my dad? If she does, then what happens? Will my dad ever speak to me again? Will he tell her that I've been lying? Then who will my gran believe?

I wish I had listened to Jude. I wish I had listened to my mum. I wish I had never gone by our house. I wish I had never seen what I saw. What I've done is something that my gran's wishing tree can never, ever undo. I wipe the tears from my eyes and sit up straight. Whatever happens, I have to face my punishment. This is all my fault.

I hear my gran sigh. She turns to me.

'Johnson,' she says – and I'm surprised to hear there is no anger in her voice – 'you know how much I love you, don' you?'

'Yes, Gran.'

I'm so relieved I almost cry all over again. She sits down and takes my hand in hers.

'There goin' to be a lot of strange stuff happenin' in the comin' days an' weeks,' she says. 'There goin' to be a lot of stuff you an' you young min' ain' goin' to understand. Things is goin' to get worse 'fore they get better. But I want you to know that everyt'ing's goin' to be all right. Everyt'ing goin' to turn out fine. I know this, 'cos I seen it. You know how you gran can see things, don't you, Johnson? You know how you gran can see stuff that's goin' to happen tomorrow an' next week an' sometimes beyon' that. I'm always here for you, no matter what happen. You understand?' She touches my cheek. 'This place, this hill, will always be a safe place for you. Remember that. You promise me?'

'Yes, Gran, I promise.'

I say these words. The truth is, I don't know what my gran is talking about, but if she says everything will be all right, I know that it will be. I'm not in trouble. Nothing is going to happen to me. I'm safe. These are the words that stay with me.

CHAPTER 3

Jude has left for the bus that will take him to senior school in Sauteurs. After Jill has made breakfast she will head off to school too. She goes to the Samaritan Presbyterian School at the bottom of the village, where I will start in a few weeks' time. Mummy is still sick in bed. No one knows what is wrong with her, but she has a fever. It's down to Jill and me to get Jemeela, Jeffrey, Jeffon and Jade ready for the day. When Jill goes to school, Jade will be looked after by my nan, while Jemeela and me stick around and keep an eye on Jeffrey and Jeffon.

My first duty is to get the water. The public water pipe is opposite my nan's house. The journey down is easy. Carrying two full buckets back up the hill is hard.

By the time I get back home my dad is at work. As soon as he wakes he walks up the road to Miss Anne's place and puts her cow out to pasture behind her house. Then he goes and works in the fields. Some days he picks bananas, some days nutmeg or cocoa, sometimes all of these things. It depends on the time of year and what Old Man Baptiste has planned for him. When he has finished he might put in a few hours helping Devlin deliver building supplies. Then he goes to the bar or out drinking with friends. We hardly ever see him and we don't have any money. No wonder my mum is sick.

Our breakfast is always the same: hot, sugary water and a piece of bread or, if we have them, crackers. Jill is making dumplings to go with the bananas that we'll eat for lunch. She keeps prodding me and telling me what to do. But I know what I'm doing. We all have jobs around the house and I take mine seriously. Jemeela is the one who scrubs Jeffrey and Jeffon in the shower; I'm the one who feeds them.

'Johnson,' Jill says, 'what's the matter with Jeffrey?'

Jeffrey is leaning back in his chair, his face tilted towards the ceiling; his eyes are rolled back. I feel his forehead with my wrist. There's nothing wrong with him. He's tired, that's all. Last night Daddy woke the whole house when he tripped over the chair on the porch and fell through the front door, then tried to get into the big bed in our room, thinking it was his own.

I pick up Jeffrey and put him back on the bed. I watch over him till his eyelids grow heavy again.

When I get back to the kitchen Jill has finished preparing the lunch. She places a large metal plate over the pot containing the dumplings to keep away the flies.

'We need water,' she says. 'Almost all the water is gone. Daddy will be vex if there's no water when he come home.'

'But I just go and get the water,' I say.

Jill makes a face. 'I done me duties, an' now I have to go to school. You still got t'ings to do. We need more water.'

She dries her hands and calls out to Jemeela, who is hanging clothes on the line under the house.

The buckets feel even heavier this time, as I head back up the hill, and I have to stop a lot to catch my breath.

*

On the slopes above me are Old Man Baptiste's cherry trees. Old Man Baptiste is the richest man in the village. He has hundreds of cherry trees. Cherries make me think of my gran. The one thing she doesn't have in her garden is a cherry tree. I get an idea. When I take her water I'll also bring her some cherries. My gran loves her fruit. Cherries will make her feel better. Old Man Baptiste has plenty of trees.

I tip the water out of one of the buckets and hide the other in the long grass. I dart into the orchard. I creep through the trees until I'm in the middle, surrounded by Old Man Baptiste's ripe red cherries. I jump up, grab hold of a branch and swing into a tree. I pick the cherries as fast as I can and drop them into the bucket beneath me. In next to no time the bucket is half full. It's time to go.

As I drop to the ground I lift my head and see a pair of legs, bare from the knee down. My heart starts to pound. But it isn't Old Man Baptiste; it's my father. In his left hand he's holding a bottle of beer. In his right is his belt. A look of rage spreads across his face. He takes a step towards me and raises his belt. My father has never, ever hit me before. 'Daddy, please …' I cry.

He starts to tell me he's been looking for me all over the village, but I know this isn't true. He must have been lying in the grass, drinking his beer somewhere nearby, and seen me as I crept into the orchard.

'The cherries ain' for me, Daddy,' I say. 'I pick them for Gran …'

'You's a t'ief,' he says. 'Me son is a t'ief.'

He's so drunk he can barely get the words out. In the space of a few seconds I weigh up my choices. I can either stay here and get a whipping or I can make a run for it to my gran's. Even though she's sick, my dad would never dare head up to her place when he's drunk. She would cuss him something rotten and if my dad is scared of anyone it's her. I drop the bucket and run. The belt buckle whooshes past my ear. I reach the edge of the orchard and look back.

My father is still on his feet, but swaying. I run as fast as I can and don't stop until I reach my gran's little house.

The door is open. It always is. I tiptoe inside. I don't want to wake her if she's asleep. But the bed is empty. Maybe she has gone to the toilet or maybe she has wandered down to my grandpa's grave. I go round the back of the house and call out her name. I stop and listen, but hear nothing except for the wind in the trees.

Now I start to worry. I know that my gran is not well. What if she has wandered off and something has happened to her? Maybe she has taken a fall? Maybe she has broken a leg? What if she's hit her head?

As I start down the path that leads to my grandpa's grave, I see some movement out of the corner of my eye. I turn and it's Jemeela. She's standing at the top of the path.

'Johnson,' she says, 'come quickly. Mummy needs you.'

'But Gran …'

'Gran's not here …' She starts to cry. 'Please, Johnson. Come quickly.'

She turns and hurries back down the path. I follow her. Jemeela runs fast and I don't catch her till she gets to our house. I no longer care about my dad. My gran is gone. Something is very wrong. I run into our kitchen, but nobody's there. There's no one in our bedroom either. I hear voices coming from my parents' room. I open the door. The blinds are drawn, but there is light streaming through the cracks.

My mother is propped up in bed. Lying next to her are Jeffrey and Jeffon. Jemeela is standing by the door, wiping the tears from her face. There's someone standing beside her. A woman. I can't see her face.

'Come here,' my mother says weakly.

She pats the bed beside her. I sit down.

'Yes, Mummy?'

I wait. My mother draws a breath. Her lungs wheeze.

'Gran is sick,' she says. 'They come and take her away jus' now in an ambulance.' She touches my hand. 'She goin' to be OK, Johnson, but it will take a while before she be better. She need rest.'

'It's her diabetes,' Jemeela blurts.

My little sister is only seven, but she's smart and clever, like Jude and Jill. She picks up a lot. I know that my gran has a bad heart and that there's something wrong with her blood. Maybe that is what diabetes is. My mum's fingers curl around mine.

'The doctors come and take a look at me too,' she says. 'They don't like what they see. They want to make some tests in the hospital. That's why your Auntie Abigail is here.'

I turn. My father's sister, Abigail, takes a step forward.

'Hello, Johnson,' she says. Her voice is cold. It always is.

She's painfully thin. The only time she brightens up is when she's around Ainsley, my cousin. But Ainsley isn't here. He must be at home with Harrison, Abigail's husband. I have a really bad feeling.

'You be goin' to stay with your auntie for a while,' my mum says. 'Till everybody be better.'

I don't know whether she's talking about herself, my gran or my dad – or all three. It doesn't much matter. My world is falling apart. I bite my lip. Whatever happens, I'm not going to cry in front of my brothers and sisters. And I'm certainly not going to cry in front of Abigail. I'm gripping my mum's hand like a vice. I want to let go, but I can't.

'Why can't I help Jill and Jemeela?'

My mum touches my face. My nan and Ena can only cope with so many extra mouths, she says. The house is full as it is. Jude will stay with his grandparents – his father's parents – in Victoria. My nan will look after Jade. Jill will do whatever she can, whenever she can, to look after Jeffrey and Jeffon, but when she has to go to school Jemeela will step in. Ena still has to run the shop.

Turning to Abigail, my mum says thank God we have the love and support of my dad's sister at this difficult time. Abigail takes a step forward and puts her hands on my shoulders.

'Come, Johnson.'

'It will only be for a short time,' my mother says.

She sits up, takes my hand and presses it to her cheek.

'But why me? Why me?' I say.

My mother has no answer. She falls back exhausted and closes her eyes. Abigail's hands are still on my shoulders. I feel them tighten their grip.

'Go and get your t'ings,' she says. 'It's a long walk to Red Mud.'

CHAPTER 4

The walk from Diego Piece takes an hour, and we do not say a word to each other the whole way. Abigail walks at an amazing pace and doesn't stop – not once. But she has shoes and I don't. And she has an umbrella to shade her from the hot sun and I don't.

'Let's be clear about somet'ing right away,' she barks, as soon as we walk in through her kitchen door. 'You are me brother's son and I'm takin' you in 'cos this is a bad business, a very bad business. I want to help you mammy any way I can. Everybody can see how terrible she sufferin'. But there's rules in this house, Johnson Beharry, an' I won't tolerate no disrespect. Is that clear?'

'Yes, Tan Abigail.'

Abigail's house is smaller than ours. It has one bedroom, a kitchen and a sitting room. Given how my auntie is, I'm surprised by the state of the place. There are unwashed dishes in the tub by the window and a thick layer of dust under my feet. I can see Harrison through a crack in the bedroom door. He's asleep on the bed.

'I may not live in Deego Pee,' Abigail says, 'but I know

people there. I talk to them. I know how you's disappearin'
into the bush all the day long, lookin' for rats an' mice an'
Lord knows what else up in them hills. There'll be no runnin'
off for as long as you's here under me roof. Is that clear?'

'Yes, Tan Abigail.'

Ainsley asks his mother when I can come out to play.

'First t'ings first.'

She produces a sack – the kind they use for bagging up
cocoa and nutmeg – and points to the floor on the other
side of the kitchen table. This is where I'm to sleep. Then she
tells me what I have to do to earn my keep. I must get into a
routine. She starts to go through the list. There are animals
that need feeding before the rest of the house wakes up: a
cow, a donkey, a goat, a rabbit and a cockerel.

When this is done I must prepare breakfast, wait for
Abigail, Harrison and Ainsley to wake up, then sit down
and eat myself. Afterwards I will wash the dishes, clear
everything away and sweep the courtyard.

'Can we play now?' Ainsley asks.

Abigail shakes her head.

'Go wake you father.'

Harrison appears a minute later, rubbing his eyes.

'Hey, Johnson,' he says.

We shake hands. Harrison is tall and easy-going, but I'm
wary of him. He leads me and Ainsley outside. There's a
large nutmeg tree in the middle of the courtyard. I feel a stab

of longing for home; it reminds me of the nutmeg tree that stands outside our house. I already know that Abigail hates leaves. Harrison points out the brush that I'm to use to clear them: a bunch of twigs tied with twine around an old broom handle. It's so old I'd be better off picking them up with my hands.

At the back of the yard is a lean-to. The lean-to is divided into pens. In the first pen is a donkey, in the second a goat and in the third a cow. The cow provides milk. The goat's milk is turned into cheese. Harrison doesn't say what the donkey is for. His fur is patchy and one ear flops down over his face. He looks too old and tired to carry anybody.

Harrison owns a plot of land up in the hills where he grows fruit and vegetables. The donkey carries him up the track and the produce back down. They have a cockerel too. He's all that's left of a load of poultry after a wild dog got into the yard a few months back. Abigail, Harrison and Ainsley were out at the time, but a neighbour saw what happened. They have a rabbit and that got attacked by the dog as well. Ainsley grabs my hand and shows me the rabbit in his pen. Half of one of his ears is bitten off and one back leg is broken. He hops with a limp. The rabbit only survived, Ainsley tells me, because of the cockerel.

'The cockerel?'

'When our neighbour hear all the commotion, he come around to find the cockerel fightin' the dog,' Harrison says.

'The neighbour say the dog lose an eye, 'cos of the way the cockerel go at him.'

I look around me at the state of the yard. I can see where Harrison has put chicken wire to stop dogs getting in over the gate again. The wire is held up by two thin sticks and looks like it will blow over in the next storm.

The rabbit run is also in a bad way. The frame has been pegged to the ground with stakes, but if a dog wants to get in, it can dig under it. The donkey *ee-aws* so loud that Ainsley jumps. Then the cow and the goat start. Next the cockerel crows. In a second the whole place has gone completely crazy. Even the rabbit starts jumping around, throwing himself at the walls of the run.

From inside the house Abigail yells and Harrison runs over and smacks the donkey and the cow until they stop hollering.

'Abigail, she hates the noise,' Harrison says. 'Jus' make sure you feed 'em nice an' speedy. An' if that don't work, give 'em a whack.'

He shows me the shed where he keeps the dried grass for the cow and the donkey; and a bin full of slug-eaten cabbage, carrot and sweet potato for the goat and the rabbit. I spend the rest of the morning picking up leaves and doing the housework.

By the time I've finished washing the dishes and getting water from the standpipe, the tree has dropped more leaves and I have to sweep the yard again.

When we sit down and eat – the first time that I've stopped all day – I think about my family. I worry about my mum and my gran and wonder whether they're OK. I think about Jill, Jemeela, Jeffrey, Jeffon and Jade at my nan's. If only I were with them, I know I'd be able to help. Instead I'm here, looking after Abigail and her family. It makes no sense.

After dinner I clear away the dishes and wash up. Then I help Harrison settle the animals for the night. The cockerel goes into the pen with the rabbit; the donkey, the cow and the goat pretty much look after themselves. I watch Harrison check the bolts on the gate.

'You know that a wild dog could get in again and kill the baby rabbits and the new chickens you goin' to get,' I say.

'You think?' he asks me, giving the wire above the gate a shake.

'I'm just thinking out loud,' I tell him.

Harrison looks at me. It's too dark to see his face, but I can almost hear the thoughts running through his head.

'You like to fix things, don't you?'

'I could fix his whole yard up pretty good,' I tell him.

'That's cool.'

He wanders back into the house.

I go to bed that night holding the hammer from the bag of tools that Kellon's dad gave me before I left Diego Piece. Kellon's dad knows I like to make things and the hammer will be a comfort to me, he says. I have to use my clothes as a pillow and the sack prickles my skin, but if I concentrate really hard I can hear the sound of the wind in the nutmeg tree and this helps me to get to sleep.

*

Abigail comes back one day to tell me that my mother is in hospital in Victoria with a sickness called meningitis. The doctors say she's lucky, as meningitis can kill. She'll be back in Diego Piece in a week. Meanwhile my gran has left the hospital and is resting up with my Aunt Jane. The doctors have given her medicine for her diabetes, but have told her that she needs to take things easy, as she has another kind of sickness on top of the diabetes: high blood pressure.

I ask Abigail what this means and she says it can place a strain on Gran's heart. This is why she needs to take things easy.

Jane is Abigail's sister. Sometimes I wonder how. Jane has a smile as big as her heart and she hugs each and every one of us whenever she comes to visit. She lives in a place called Annandale on the edge of the capital, St George's, and helps her husband Chris run a car-repair yard. I thank God that my gran is in good hands. It helps me to look on the bright side. Soon my mum will be back in Diego Piece and when my dad comes to his senses and stops his drinking, she'll go back to him. This is what I tell myself when I lie awake at night, listening to the wind as she moves through the branches of the nutmeg tree.

CHAPTER 5

My first day of school.

The class is packed with desks and chairs. There's one small window and although it's wide open, the air is so hot and sticky I feel as if I can't breathe. I'm seated in the middle of the room, halfway between the wall and the window and halfway between Mr Sweeny's desk and the back of the class. I tug at the neck of my T-shirt and stare out of the window. From my desk I can see the base of the hill that leads to my gran's little house. Seeing it makes me feel better.

I'm in a state of shock. For years Jude and Jill have been telling me how much they love school, but I'm wondering which part they can possibly mean. I would like to sit next to my friend, Kellon, but I can't. Instead I get to sit by a girl called Roxanne, who comes to school with exercise books and a pencil case that's bulging with pens, pencils and crayons. She keeps staring at something under her desk. When I catch her eye she looks away quickly and smiles, as if she's doing something wrong and doesn't want anybody to know about it. After a while I realize she's staring at something under my desk, not hers. I look too, but the only thing I see is my two bare feet. I look around and finally understand what Roxanne is looking at: I'm the only child in the class without shoes.

When she stares at my feet again I dig her in the ribs. I do it with my elbow and barely touch her, but she cries out like a baby. Mr Sweeny, who is drawing on the blackboard, snaps his head around. Who has made a disturbance in his class?

There's laughter from behind me. Mr Sweeny reaches into his pocket, produces his strap – a short piece of leather with a grip at one end – and brings it down hard on the edge of his desk. Roxanne jumps. Then she starts to cry. The class goes very quiet. Mr Sweeny has already told us that he won't stand for any nonsense. Troublemakers will get the strap across the palm of their hand. Those that make trouble a lot will get sent to Mr Mark, the headmaster, and Jude says he has a strap that hurts even more.

Roxanne's tears splash across a picture of a house she has drawn on the cover of her exercise book, smudging the ink and making it run. I put my hand up.

'I did it, Mr Sweeny,' I say. 'I make her cry out.'

'What is your name?' he asks.

Johnson, I tell him.

'Your last name, boy?'

'Beharry, sir.'

Mr Sweeny puts his piece of chalk down. He takes off his glasses, rests them on the edge of his desk and stares at me.

'What did you do?'

'I dig me elbow into her.'

'Why?' he asks.

I've nothing to say. I'm not going to tell Mr Sweeny that I dug my elbow into Roxanne's ribs because she's staring at my bare feet.

'I don't know, sir.'

'Let's see what you do know,' he says, and beckons me to the front of the class with his long, bony finger.

'What is this?' he asks, pointing at the shape that he has just drawn on the blackboard. It looks like a sweet potato, but I know that if I say it's a sweet potato everyone in the class will laugh and then I really am in trouble.

'It's our island. It's Grenada, sir.'

Mr Sweeny nods. He looks pleased.

'And how big is our island?' he says.

'It's twenty miles from the top of Grenada and it's ten miles across,' I tell Mr Sweeny.

He nods again and manages to look even more pleased. The incident with Roxanne is forgotten. He asks me to sit down.

As I take my place, Roxanne checks that Mr Sweeny is facing the blackboard, then she sticks her tongue out at me from behind her exercise book.

Mr Sweeny has drawn lines across his map, dividing the island into six parts.

'Does anyone know what these are?' he asks.

Several children put their hands up. I don't, even though I know the answer: they're the six parishes that make up the island. I can't see the point. I can get all this from my gran and from Jude and Jill. I know that St Andrew's, on the eastern side of the island, is the biggest parish and that we live in the smallest, St Mark's.

I know that Queen Elizabeth II of Great Britain is also the Queen of Grenada, but because she doesn't live here we have to have a prime minister, a Grenadian, to rule over us. I know that Grenada, Carriacou and Petit Martinique are the three main islands of the Grenadines and that Grenada is far and away the largest. I even know that ninety thousand people live on the island. I know that we're very lucky, because Grenada, being at the southern end of our ocean, the Caribbean, gets very few hurricanes and that God, who sends the hurricanes, must be a Grenadian, because the last one we got, Hurricane Janet, was more than thirty years ago, when my mum was a little girl. I know the power of a hurricane, because my mum has told me how she remembers seeing sheets of galvanized steel and whole roofs flying through the air as she fled from her house to a neighbour's.

I know that nutmeg and cocoa are the island's main crops. Almost all my relatives have been involved in picking and delivering these crops, one way or another, ever since my great grandfather, Joseph Gunpot, arrived in Grenada from India a hundred years ago. The exceptions were my Grand Uncle Bill, who became a millionaire from setting up Grenada's very first bus company, and my Aunt Jane and Uncle Chris, who own a garage on the outskirts of St George's. I'm quite certain that my Grand Uncle Bill never attended a day of school in his life. And I know for sure that Uncle Chris never learned how to fix a car by sitting in a classroom. One way or another I will do everything I possibly can to get out of school. School is for Jill and Jude. It's not for me.

*

One day Kellon and I are playing cricket during break when I spot Jill sitting at the base of a grassy bank, her head in her hands. I recognize the red ribbons in her hair. I run over. When she looks up, her face is wet from crying.

'Oh, Johnson,' she says, 'where have you been?'

My first thought is that I'm in trouble with Mr Sweeny or the headmaster, Mr Mark, because yesterday I bunked off school, playing with my new friends – Stephen, Gregory, Dexter and Joshua in their den in the woods above the school. They've shown me and Kellon a way of getting out of lessons: by volunteering to work in the kitchens for a roly-poly cook called Mavis. After we're done in the kitchens we take off into the woods and hide out in the den – a cave at the bottom of a rocky outcrop – where nobody notices we're missing. Or so I thought. Now, suddenly, I'm afraid.

'What is going to happen to me?' I ask.

My sister frowns and wipes away her tears.

'What is going to happen to you? Nothing is going to happen to you.'

'Then what are you talking about?'

'It's Mummy,' she says. 'She just stop by the school.'

Now that my mum is back from hospital, there are too many people at my nan's for my aunt to be able to cope. My father is still drinking, so going home is out of the question. Where am I going to live?

CHAPTER 6

I need to earn money, and there's only one place around here where there's work, and that's Old Man Baptiste's nutmeg plantations.

I've no idea how old Old Man Baptiste is. He could be sixty or he could be a hundred. People can't remember a time when he was young. He seems to have been old and bad-tempered for ever. His body is thin and short, his skin looks grey and he has a patchy white beard. Long hairs sprout from his nostrils and ears. His round glasses, sunburned forehead and beak of a nose give him a look of Mahatma Gandhi, the Indian independence leader who we're learning about at school. But Old Man Baptiste is interested in the rewards of this life – he's only out for himself.

I find him in one of his nutmeg plantations high above the village, cussing a worker for damaging one of his trees. I can see no sign of damage, but Old Man Baptiste, with his funny, high-pitched voice, is ranting about the growing cycle of the nutmeg: how it takes five years or even six to tell the sex of a tree, how only the female trees bear fruit and how none will grow for at least two years after the male trees have been identified and separated from the female ones.

'My trees are precious – more precious than any cow, sheep or goat – and this is how you treat them,' he bellyaches, before turning on his heel and nearly walking straight into me. 'You . . .' he says. 'Are you come to steal my damn fruit?'

Old Man Baptiste doesn't frighten me. I guess it would be different if I depended on him for my living, like most people in the village, but I don't. I smile and shake my head. It's all I can do not to say something that will make his blood boil. He breaks every one of my gran's golden rules. He loves no one, except himself, and he respects no one, not even himself. Which is why he doesn't have, and never will have, my respect. But today, for the first time in my life, I need Old Man Baptiste, so I tell myself: be careful.

I've thought about this moment for days. What I will say. How I will say it. I look Old Man Baptiste directly in the eye and tell him I want him to give me a job. He laughs. A couple of nearby fruit pickers risk their jobs by stopping what they're doing and listening in.

'Give me one good reason why I should employ you. You're a child – and you savage my trees when my back is turned.'

'Mr Baptiste, sir,' I say, 'I can give you many good reasons.'

He stands there, sneering at me.

'Go on then.'

'First, you should know that I'm a hard worker. When

I come here I will not sleep and I will not skive.'

'Well,' he snorts, 'that will be something of a novelty. Everyone says they will work hard, but nobody knows the meaning of the word. Every damn one of you ends up skiving. You're all the same – you want money for nothing.'

'Second, I can climb any tree in your plantation without a ladder.'

'That I do believe! You're in and out of them the whole time, stealing my fruit.'

'I don't drink rum or beer,' I tell him, 'so I will never get drunk and damage your trees.'

'But you've already damaged my trees,' he says. 'You and that friend of yours leave bite marks in my fruit. You think I don't know?'

I look him straight in the eye.

'That's another good reason why you should give me a job. If you give me a job I will stop leaving bite marks in your fruit.'

'But this is blackmail!' Old Man Baptiste shouts.

I'm not a hundred per cent sure what blackmail is, but if blackmail is about getting what you want, whatever it takes, then I guess he's right. I start to feel nervous. I think I might be close to getting what I want.

'The most important thing,' I tell him, 'is, if you give me a job I will work for no money.'

His eyes narrow.

'If you don't want money, what do you want?'

'I want a pair of shoes.'

I've never owned a pair of shoes in my life. If I have shoes I can save fifteen minutes when I walk from Red Mud to Diego Piece. If I have shoes I can sweep Abigail's yard, the job I hate most, in half the time. I won't have to pick thorns and splinters out of my feet every ten seconds. I've worked it all out in my head. I need to be able to spend as long as possible helping my mum at the little wooden house she's found to live in.

In the last week my cousin Ron, Kellon and I have turned the place around. We have re-hung the door and built up the broken pillar so that the shack no longer leans down the valley. We have plugged all the holes in the roof, and the place has started to dry out.

'Shoes?' Old Man Baptiste says. He's not laughing now. He's trying to see where the trickery lies. 'What kind of shoes?'

'Four weeks' work for a pair of flip-flops,' I tell him.

I can see Old Man Baptiste making calculations in his head.

'A pair of flip-flops will take six weeks' work.'

The best thing I've learned since I've been at the Samaritan Presbyterian is the meaning of the word 'truce'. This is what I'm offering Old Man Baptiste, and he knows it. He holds out his hand.

I tell him that there is one more thing. It will cost him nothing, but I can't do without it. I need six large empty crates. The kind he uses to box up his fruit. I tell Old Man Baptiste I will accept the flip-flops as payment when I've finished my six weeks. But the crates I need now.

Old Man Baptiste's thin, bony hand is still outstretched. I put my hand in his and shake on it.

CHAPTER 7

In the weeks that follow I get up, feed the animals, clean the house, sweep the yard, make the breakfast and get Ainsley ready for school. I attend two, sometimes three classes in the morning, then work in the kitchens until lunch.

As soon as I've eaten I take off up the hill and hang in the cave with Gregory, Stephen, Dexter and Joshua, who are starting to spend so little time at school they may as well not be there at all. Nobody seems to care whether I'm there either. Abigail is only interested in Ainsley and Mr Sweeny is happy as long as there is order in his class. Everyone around me is too wrapped up in their own problems to know what I'm up to, and this suits me just fine. There's something else I need to build first – a surprise for my mum's birthday.

I've stashed Old Man Baptiste's crates in the den, right at the back of the cave. They're all damaged in some way, but it doesn't matter. I'm making her a bed, in two three-foot sections, with legs at each corner. This way I can carry them to the shack one at a time. When I get there I will screw the two sections together and nail down the slats that support the mattress. It's starting to take shape. I can't wait to see my mum's face when I give it to her.

After about forty minutes' work on the bed, I run up to the plantation. I work there for an hour, sometimes two, picking cocoa and nutmeg, then rush back to school to collect Ainsley and walk him home.

After six weeks, as we agreed, I go to Old Man Baptiste and ask for my shoes. On Friday – payday – he hands them over: white flip-flops with red straps and red soles. My first pair of shoes.

I want to tell everyone, but I tell only Ainsley, on condition that he doesn't tell his mum. If Abigail sees my flip-flops she'll want to know how I came by them. And then the whole story will come out – school, skiving, my deal with Old Man Baptiste, everything.

I'm exhausted, but it takes me a long time to get to sleep. There is a lot to think about: the bed, my shoes and another piece of good news – something that Abigail let slip over dinner. My gran is coming home in two weeks' time. I can see light at the end of my tunnel.

The next morning Abigail sends me over to Diego Piece to pick up some shopping from the store at the bottom of the village. Thanks to my new shoes the walk between the two villages is no longer a hardship. But when I get to the store the sports bag that I hand over is filled with so much stuff – milk, tins of meat, butter, rice, sugar and flour – that I can hardly lift it. After several attempts I work out that if I put the bag on my back, with one of the straps on my forehead, I can go a couple of hundred yards before I have to stop and rest. But in the high heat every step becomes a struggle and it's several hours before I make it back to Red Mud. Before I get to the door I take off my flip-flops and tuck them into the waistband of my shorts, under my T-shirt.

Abigail is out in the yard. I slip my flip-flops inside my rolled-up bedding and put the bag of shopping on the kitchen table. In walks Abigail, followed by Harrison and Ainsley. She's holding a broom and sweating. She's in a foul temper; clearing up leaves is her least favourite job.

'Where you been?' she yells. 'It's been three hours since you been gone.'

She goes crazy about everything – the state of the yard, the fact that she, Harrison and Ainsley are starving because they've been waiting for me. I try to tell her that the shopping was heavy and I could hardly lift it, but she tells me to be quiet. I'm lying, she says. I gotta be.

'You been skivin'. I just know it. You and that friend of yours. Skivin' when you uncle, you little cousin an' me are goin' out of our minds with hunger.'

I know better than to argue with Abigail when she's in one of these moods. It's better to say nothing and wait for it to blow over like a passing storm.

She opens the bag. A vex kind of look passes across her face. She picks up the bag and carries it to the back door, where she holds it up to the light.

'Come here,' she says quietly.

My blood runs cold. I walk over to her. Suddenly Abigail grabs the back of my neck and forces my face into the bag. One of the jars has broken and molten butter has gone everywhere. The sugar and flour bags have split open. Everything except for the tins is ruined.

'How did this happen?' she screams. 'How?'

I can't think. But as her grip tightens on my neck it comes to me. When I stopped and rested one time, I must have set the bag down too quickly. If a rock was underneath, it would have smashed the jar. I pull myself away and rush to the other side of the table.

Abigail runs after me. She screams for Harrison and Ainsley to do something, but they just stand there, as shocked by her anger as I am. Abigail knows she can't catch me. No matter how quickly she moves, I always manage to keep the table between us. She picks up my bedding and lashes it across the table like a whip. It misses me but hits the table and splits, sending something flying across the room. One of my shiny red and white flip-flops lands with a plop at Harrison's feet.

Everybody stares at it. Then they look at me. There's nothing I can do except stand and watch as Abigail plunges her hand inside the sack. With a look of triumph she holds up the other shoe. She asks in a low and trembling voice exactly how I've come to own a bright, shiny new pair of flip-flops.

I stand with my hands behind my back and say nothing; there's nothing I can say. Abigail decides that I must have stolen the flip-flops; that I'm a dirty, rotten t'ief.

I hold my breath, but Ainsley springs forward with tears streaming down his face and throws his arms around me.

'He not a t'ief,' he shouts at his mother. 'Johnson work hard for he shoes. He pick fruit for Old Man Baptiste and Old Man Baptiste pay him wit' a pair of shoes.'

Ainsley knows the whole story. It doesn't take too much longer for everything to come out. Abigail hands my flip-flops to Ainsley with a warning that if he dares give them back to me he'll find himself in as much trouble as I am. Then she says that she, Harrison and Ainsley are going to Diego Piece to replace the food I've just ruined, and to order some 'galvanized', a big sheet of corrugated galvanized steel. They need it as a new roof for the lean-to, because when it rains, water pours through the holes, soaking the donkey, the cow and the goat. I know it is the feed they're thinking of, not the animals.

After they leave I stand by the nutmeg tree, watching a huge bank of thunderclouds roll up the valley. Suddenly the heavens open. The rain lashes down and soon I'm standing in my bare feet in a huge puddle. Leaves float on the water like tiny boats. I watch them swirling this way and that as they're blown by the wind. Abigail doesn't want to find a single leaf on the ground when she gets back. This was her parting shot to me as she left the house.

I walk over to the animals. Water is pouring through a hole in the roof on to the donkey's head. I look at him and he looks at me. I put my arms around his neck and bury my face in his fur. I tell him how sorry I am and how much I will miss him. I tell him I have to leave and that I hope he understands.

It's my mum's birthday. I will present her with the bed, then break the news that I've left my aunt's for good. Abigail is not my mum's sister; she's my dad's sister. My mum used to say that the drinking is like a sickness with my dad. I will tell my mum, maybe the sickness that makes my dad drink comes out in a different way with Abigail. Either way I'm not going back.

An hour after I walk out of Abigail's house I reach the den. I sit for a while in the mouth of the cave as another storm cloud passes overhead. One more time I go over what I'm going to tell my mum. I can make myself useful in the shack. I can wash clothes, I can cook, I can help Jill and my mum look after the little ones. I can even bring in some extra money by working for Old Man Baptiste.

I pick up the pieces of the bed, one on each shoulder, and set off towards the shack. As I approach it I know something is wrong. Normally either my mum or Jill is outside doing the washing or cooking a meal. Today everything is quiet and the door of the shack is shut. I put the pieces of the bed on the ground and push the door back. The shack is empty. It isn't simply that there is nobody inside; there is nothing inside. No clothes. No food. Everything that was here two days ago is gone. All my life, thanks to my gran, I've seen the forest as a magical place, but now, surrounded by the rocks and the trees, I see it differently.

My imagination runs riot. Maybe somebody came up here and killed my family. Or maybe the spirits of the forest – the manicou – took them. Stop it, I tell myself. What would the spirits of the forest want with my brothers' and sisters' clothes? If Jill was here she would remind me that I'm nine years old – old enough to use my brain. So think, Johnson, think.

I sit down and think, and the answer pops into my head. If anybody knows what has happened, it will be Ena. I pick up the bed and set off down towards the village.

CHAPTER 8

As I break through the trees Diego Piece is spread out before me. Sunlight races across the rooftops, chasing the clouds' shadows away. Ena is sitting at her table in the shop, jotting down sums on a piece of paper. She looks up and sees me standing in the doorway.

'Johnson,' she says, 'what in the worl' you carryin'?'

I put the pieces of the bed down. My shoulders hurt where the wood has dug into my skin.

'Where's Mummy?' I ask. 'Where's everybody?'

She replies, like it's the most natural thing in the world, 'They're at home, Treasure.'

'Home? You mean, me gran's place?'

'No, Treasure,' she says. 'Your home. Nobody tell you? They move back in las' night. They back with you daddy again.'

Ena is still talking as I pick up the bed and start to run up the road. I focus on the base of the hill at the top of the village. The pieces of bed knock against each other, making a clack-clack sound as I run. I ignore the pain in my shoulders where the wood digs into my skin. Soon I no longer feel the weight of the bed or the splinters in my feet or the heat of the sun on my head. I cut through the trees, dodging the sharp thorns that reach out towards my bare legs.

Ahead I hear laughter – the laughter of my brothers and sisters. I stop as I reach the edge of the trees, the place where I once stood and watched my father collapse in a drunken heap under the house. What I see now helps me to rub out the memory of that day. My father is standing on the balcony, surrounded by his children. He's holding Jade in his outstretched arms. He's tickling Jade and Jade is laughing. Jeffrey is holding one of my father's legs and Jeffon the other. They're standing next to the chair where I used to sit with my dad and leaf through the pages of Motor magazine.

Through the window I can see my mother moving around the kitchen. Jemeela and Jill are in there too – I can hear Jill bossing my little sister as they help my mum with the cooking.

As I step out of the trees Jeffrey and Jeffon see me and come tearing down the steps. They ask what I'm carrying and suddenly I feel really stupid. My mum has the best birthday present she could possibly ask for – she's back home. She has no need for a bed. She and Daddy already have one.

'You built that?' Jeffon asks.

I nod.

'Why?' Jeffrey asks. 'Why did you build a bed?'

It's a simple question, but I don't know what to tell him.

My family is here – they're back home – and nobody told me.

Watched by my father, I climb the steps, dragging the bits of the bed with me. I walk through the kitchen into our bedroom. I set down the pieces and tip my tools on to the floor. I'm fixing the two main sections together with the first screw when I hear the door open behind me. The wood is hard and the screw goes in with difficulty. I grit my teeth and twist the screwdriver. My father says my name, but I don't stop what I'm doing; I don't turn around. I don't want to talk to him. I don't want to talk to my mother. I don't want to talk to anyone. All I want is to get the bed finished. It's no longer my mother's bed. It's my bed. This is where I will sleep.

'What are you doing?' my father asks. 'Johnson …?'

I say nothing. I carry on working.

'I ask what you're doing …'

Still I carry on.

'Johnson, look at me when I talk to you.'

I turn round. I can feel tears behind my eyes. I taste them in my throat, but I'm not going to cry. This is my home. My bedroom. My bed. I'm not going to cry.

My father is in the doorway. Abigail is standing next to him. The sight of her kills the urge in me to cry. I turn back to the bed. If I can just finish it, I tell myself, there will be no cause to send me back to Red Mud.

'What are you doing here?' Daddy asks. There's anger in his voice now.

'I's not going back,' I say, as I twist another screw into the bed frame. 'Me brothers and me sisters are all here. This is where I goin' to stay.'

'You're goin' back to Red Mud with Abigail,' my father says.

I look at the bed. The screws have gone in well. The frame is sturdy. Now to put the slats across, ready for a mattress.

I reach into the bag and take out the bundle of planks, but before I can undo the string that ties them together my father walks across the room and pulls me to my feet. He twists me round, gripping me by the arms so I can't move. He starts shouting at me. He knows everything, he says, everything. He knows that I've been skiving off school, he knows I've been working for Old Man Baptiste on the sly when I should have been studying. He says I've abused my aunt's hospitality and brought shame on him, my mum, my brothers and my sisters because of it.

'You're going back to Red Mud,' he says, 'and that's that.'

He's going with Abigail and Harrison to see a friend who has a sheet of corrugated galvanized steel. His friend is going to sell it to Abigail. It will take an hour to do the deal. After that Abigail, Harrison and Ainsley will set off for Red Mud and I will follow them with the sheet of galvanized. Carrying it on my own is my punishment. Every step that I take between here and Red Mud will make me think about the suffering I've caused.

I listen to him, but say nothing. What is there to say? The dad I used to know is gone. When I saw him on the porch with Jade in his arms and Jeffrey and Jeffon by his legs, I thought he was back. But he's not.

He releases me, turns on his heel and slams the door behind him. I sit down on the corner of the bed and stare out of the window.

I hear whispering outside the door. It opens a crack and there is my mother. She has Jill, Jemeela, Jeffrey and Jeffon by her side. The boys cling to her skirt. My sisters look as if they want to scoop me up and hold me. But I don't move and nor do they. My mother comes and sits on the corner of the big bed. My brothers and sisters settle down beside her.

'Did you make this?' she asks, pointing at the bed.

'I made it,' I tell her. I can't bring myself to look at her as we speak. I stare at the floor.

'Did you make it for me? For my birthday?'

'I make it for myself,' I tell her. 'Nobody else.'

My mother puts her hand under my chin and raises my face to hers.

'Johnson …' she says. 'Johnson, don't be vex with me …'

'Who else is there to be vex with?' I say to her.

'Listen to me …' I can see that she's fighting back her tears. 'There are too many people under this roof. Too many mout' to feed. Your father has promised he stop his drinkin', but you know, an' I know, my beautiful son, that he's not the man he used to be. He's different. There is an anger in him. An anger that is quick to rise, an', when he lose he temper, there's no tellin' what might happen, what he might do. I don't know how t'ings goin' to work out here, I don't. But I have to try, Johnson. I have to give it a go. Raisin' a family in that shack . . .' Her voice trails away. A tear rolls down her cheek.

'But I want to be with you,' I say. 'I want to help.'

She takes my face in her hands. 'I know it can't be easy livin' with Abigail. I know how much you want to be with us . . .'

'Then why can't I be?' I say. 'Is it 'cos of something I do? Is it 'cos . . .?'

I don't want to finish what I was going to say. But I don't have to speak the words. I already know that the look in my eyes is plain for my mum to see.

'You must know,' she says, 'that I love you more than life itself. You must always remember that.'

'Then why am I the one – the only one – of all me true brothers and sisters who can't live under this roof? Why am I the one who has to be sent away?'

My mother puts her arms around me and pulls me to her.

''Cos out of all of me sweet darlin' children,' she whispers in my ear, 'you are the one I can trust – I can rely on – to get through this.'

In the end I agree, not because my mum thinks I'm the one who can look after myself, but because of a feeling I get that my dad will punish her, not me, if I don't do as she asks. I promise on the condition that I can finish building the 'little bed', as my mother calls it, and that this is where I will sleep when the time is right to come home.

When I'm done I set the little bed at right angles to the big bed and screw it to the wall. This is where it will wait for me till I'm back again.

CHAPTER 9

Twenty minutes later I go outside. Abigail, Harrison and Ainsley have already left for Red Mud. The piece of galvanized is leaning against the noni tree halfway up the path. My father is nowhere to be seen.

Jill, Jemeela and Jeffrey help me to lift it on to my back. The sun has made it very hot. The galvanized burns me through my T-shirt. I have to pour some water over it to cool it down.

'Let me help you, Johnson,' Jeffrey says. 'Let me come to Red Mud with you.'

'Just keep the little bed warm for me till I get back,' I tell him.

I pat him on the head and he smiles. I hoist the sheet of galvanized on to my back and take a few steps up the hill. I don't get more than a few feet when I feel the weight of it shift. I try gripping harder, but it keeps on sliding and I end up with two cuts across the fingers of both hands for my trouble.

Blood drips on to the path. I set the galvanized down. When Jeffrey sees the blood he says he's going to go inside and get Mummy, but I tell him not to. My mother has enough on her mind already. Instead I tell him to look for an old piece of rag while I work out how I'm going to carry the galvanized.

I go down under the house, where my father keeps all kinds of scrap. I find a long piece of string and wrap it around the top of the galvanized. I remember seeing a picture in a book that Jude brought home from school. It was about ancient Egyptians, Greeks and Romans. Jude tried to tell me about the Romans, how long their empire lasted, and which countries they conquered, but the only thing that got my attention was how the Romans built things. My favourite picture was of something called a siege tower – a huge building on wheels the Romans used for smashing down walls. The picture showed how Roman soldiers used to protect themselves from their enemies' arrows by hoisting their shields on to their backs and linking them together to form what they called a 'tortoise'. This is what I do now. By wrapping string around the top of the galvanized, I turn myself into a Roman soldier with a shield on my back.

When Jeffrey comes back with a piece of cloth, I tear it in half and wrap it around my fingers. Then I grip the string and pull the galvanized on to my back again. The string bites into the cuts, but the cloth makes the pain bearable and stops the flow of blood. I say goodbye to Jeffrey again and set off up the path.

I try not to think about the journey ahead, but because I know about time and distance, part of me is calculating how long it is going to take me to get to Red Mud. I've walked only a quarter of a mile and it has taken me twice the time it normally takes. At this rate I will not be in Red Mud till after dark and this worries me because I've never much liked the dark. The road is lined by tall trees. I try to think of the forest as the good place my gran says it is, but I know that there are bad spirits there as well as good ones; that my gran never talks about them because she doesn't like to scare me. I call on my gran now to give me courage and strength, because I can feel all mine draining through my feet with every step I take. I talk to her as if she were next to me and imagine what she would say. 'Keep walking, Johnson.

'One step at a time.

'Keep walking.

'Don' look back ...'

Suddenly there is a loud bang – something has hit the galvanized right next to my head. I peep out from under it in time to see my cousin, Ansell, arm raised, another stone in his hand. He's standing beside a big mahogany tree. He must have been hiding, waiting for me, picking his moment to hurl the stone. The noise as it hit the galvanized almost gave me a heart attack.

He drops the stone and stands there, staring at me, his hands on his hips.

'Well, if it ain' me little cousin,' he says, the scar on his face twisting his smile.

'Go away, Ansell,' I say. 'I's not in the mood.'

'What's with the galvanized?' he yells. 'You buildin' a car?'

I turn round and walk on. A second later there's another crack on the galvanized.

'Or maybe you buildin' a house for you mammy,' he shouts after me. 'I hear she be needin' one. Even somet'ing you build gotta be better than that shack she livin' in.'

I stop and turn round.

'Me mother ain' livin' in any shack,' I say. 'She at home with me dad, me brothers and me sisters.'

'But not you,' he says. 'How come?'

I walk on.

'What's the matter, Johnson?' he shouts.

I want to turn and fight, even though I know Ansell will beat me, but I hear my gran's voice telling me to keep going. As I head down the hill Ansell keeps throwing stones. Every time he hits the galvanized he laughs. His laughter rings in my ears even after I round the corner and his stones can't reach me any more.

My feet hurt, my hands hurt and I'm hot and tired and thirsty. And I've not even left Diego Piece. I have another two hours of this to go. Up ahead, on the right, is the big house with the scaffolding. Except, when I look up from under the galvanized, I see that the scaffolding is gone and the house is finished. This tells me how long it's been since I last walked along this road.

This house is the biggest in the whole of Diego Piece. It's three storeys high and has balconies on every floor. There's a lawn at the front and a tarmac drive that sweeps up from the big double gates to the door. Outside the door is a Land Rover and beyond that I can see a lush, tended nutmeg plantation. As I approach, two dogs appear from behind the Land Rover and throw themselves at the gate, barking and snarling at me.

I hear a woman's voice telling them to be quiet. I look at the house again and spot her on one of the ground-floor balconies. She's sitting on a grand chair with cushions and a high back and has a magazine in one hand and a long glass of fruit punch in the other. The thing I really notice about her is the huge pair of sunglasses. She's old enough to be my grandmother, but with her black hair and sunglasses she looks very different from my gran. My dad once showed me pictures in a magazine of a Grand Prix race that happened when he was a kid. He was always telling me about the famous drivers from those days: Graham Hill, Jackie Stewart, Jim Clark. The woman on the balcony reminds me of the women with big sunglasses who stared back at me from the pages of that magazine. The women that hung out with Graham Hill, Jackie Stewart and Jim Clark. Glamorous – that's how my father described them. That is how the woman on the balcony seems to me. Although I can't see her eyes, I know she's watching me, because her sunglasses follow me down the hill.

'Little boy,' she calls out, as I draw level with her. 'Where are you going?'

I tell her that I'm going to Red Mud.

'With no shoes?'

'I ain' got no shoes,' I say. 'I owned a pair of shoes for a day, but now me little cousin Ainsley's got them. It's lucky for him we the same size.'

She smiles and sets the magazine down.

'You're taking that piece of galvanized all the way to Red Mud?'

I tell her I am.

'Who are you?' she says. 'What's your name?'

'It's Johnson,' I tell her.

'Johnson who?'

'Johnson Beharry.'

'Well,' she says in a voice that sounds almost as if she's talking in her sleep. 'Isn't that extraordinary?'

She calls for someone to sort out the dogs. A tall thin man, old enough to be my grandfather, appears. He whistles and the dogs come to him. He grabs them by their collars and takes them inside. Then he strolls down the drive and opens the gate. I'm standing right outside. The galvanized is still on my back. We look at each other and the man smiles.

He has the kindest face I've ever seen.

'Do you know who I am?' he asks.

I shake my head.

'My name is Hammond Beharry. I'm your grand uncle. You must be Florette's boy.'

I nod my head.

'Florette's mother is my sister,' he says.

I want to tell him that I like his house, and I really like his Land Rover, but I never get the words out. Everything starts to swim before my eyes; the sky goes very dark, my legs turn to jelly and I feel myself falling.

CHAPTER 10

I'm sitting in a chair and looking at the woman with big sunglasses. We're outside, on a balcony. A fan is beating gently above my head. The woman hands me some fruit punch and I take it. I notice that my hands are shaking.

'How are you feeling?' she asks.

I touch my head.

'I'm fine, I think . . .' I look around me. How did I get here?

'You fainted. You need to drink, Johnson. You're dehydrated.'

Dehydrated. I need to drink.

'I'm your cousin, Johnson,' the woman says. 'Some people call me Babby, and some call me Syie. I'm married to your Grand Uncle Hammond.' She holds out her hand. 'Welcome.'

We shake hands.

Her husband, Grand Uncle Hammond, comes and stands behind her.

'That was a big piece of galvanized you were carrying,' he says. 'Are you feeling better?'

I nod and knock back the fruit punch in one go. Cousin

Syie asks Hammond to get me some more, then she asks to see my hands. I unfurl the pieces of cloth that are tied around my fingers. They're covered with dried blood. I try to open my fingers, but I can't. It's as if they're still wrapped around the string I fixed to the galvanized.

Cousin Syie takes off her sunglasses and studies the cuts. She looks at my grand uncle, then she turns to me.

'We need to put something on your hands, some medicine,' she says. 'You won't be walking another step this evening, young man.'

'But Cousin Syie,' I tell her, 'I have to deliver this piece of galvanized to me aunt.'

'Then Hammond can put it in the Land Rover and take it to her himself. You're not going anywhere. You're exhausted.'

'But Cousin Syie,' I say, 'my aunt will . . .'

She puts her fingers to her lips. 'Follow me.'

She leads me by the arm into the kitchen. I've never seen anything like it. There's a cooker, a fridge, a sink with taps, shelves filled with plates and glasses and, on a table in the corner, a television.

Cousin Syie washes my hands with cold water from the tap and puts some disinfectant on the cuts. The disinfectant stings terribly, but my cousin says that's a good sign. It means the medicine is working. She takes me into the sitting room and sits me down on a long settee. Across the room is the biggest television I've ever seen. Underneath it is a video. I get down on my hands and knees and look at it.

'I seen a TV before,' I tell her. 'But I never seen a video, 'cept in magazines.'

'Maybe you'd like to watch something . . .'

'I never seen a movie neither,' I say.

She asks me what I'm interested in and I tell her I like cars. She opens a cupboard and scans through a whole bunch of videos till she finds the one she's looking for. It's a movie called *Beverly Hills Cop*. She puts the video into the machine and presses 'Play'. She says I'll like it, because it has some great car chases. In the meantime she's going to make me a sandwich, while Hammond takes the galvanized to my Aunt Abigail in Red Mud.

I watch the movie, but never get to the part with the car chase. The next thing I know, I'm waking up in a bed with sheets, in a strange room. I pinch myself, because at first I think I'm dreaming. Then I remember the day before: the empty shack, the walk to my parents' home, my dad, Abigail, the galvanized, Ansell and the big house on the corner . . .

I get out of bed. I hear talking and follow the sound down a big open staircase. Grand Uncle Hammond and Cousin Syie are sitting at the kitchen table. Cousin Syie says good morning and asks what I would like to eat for breakfast.

'Breakfast?' I say.

I've slept for almost thirteen hours.

Over breakfast Cousin Syie and my grand uncle tell me

their story. She's a first cousin to my mother and Hammond is my mum's uncle. Everyone is connected to everyone else in some way in the village and even though they spent very little time in Diego Piece, they kept in touch with my mum and knew she had grown up and had a family.

'That you were sent to us is a miracle,' Cousin Syie says.

I'm not sure I understand. She takes my hands in hers.

'How would you like to come and live with us, Johnson?'

'With you? But, I . . .'

'We've spoken to your mother. I went to see her this morning.' She pauses. 'It's OK, Johnson, she told us everything.'

'There's no need for you to go back to your aunt in Red Mud,' Hammond says. 'When Syie is in England visiting family, which is a lot of the time, I'm here on my own.'

'He gets lonely,' Syie says. 'But you can be with him. You can help him on the farm. Your mummy says you like to farm.'

'I do a bit of work for Old Man Baptiste,' I say.

'We will clothe you and feed you and look after you,' Cousin Syie says. 'You'll be safe here, Johnson. What do you say?'

There is nothing to say. It's like my Cousin Syie said. It's a miracle.

The first thing Cousin Syie and my grand uncle do is take me out to buy clothes and shoes in St George's. We go in

Hammond's Land Rover. Sitting in the back, watching him work the gears and the steering wheel as we twist and turn on a road that I've only ever seen before from the seat of a bus or in my imagination, I tell myself I'm in Heaven. The Land Rover smells of oil, leather and rust. It's more than twenty years old, but it works just fine and will last another twenty years at least, Hammond says, which means he will be dead before it is.

He chuckles to himself as he says this, and Cousin Syie tells him not to be morbid. I ask what morbid means and she says it's when you dwell on bad stuff, and I tell her that that's not my way, that my gran taught me always to look on the positive. Cousin Syie tells me this is a really good thing and that she would like to get to know my gran better.

'She be comin' back from me Tan Jane's place in Annandale any day now,' I tell her. 'I miss her so much, Cousin Syie.'

She turns round and looks at me. 'It's important for you to know that you can visit your family any time you like,' she says. 'We want you to feel at home, but you must never, ever feel that you're a prisoner. You must see your mother, brothers and sisters whenever you like. You must go and visit your gran. All we expect – all we ask – is that you tell us where you are so we don't worry about you. I've promised your mother that we'll take the best possible care of you.'

'There's one other thing,' Hammond says.

'Yes, Grand Uncle?'

'Your mother tells us that you don't like school. Is that correct?'

Yes, I tell him. I don't care for school at all.

'Getting an education, Johnson, is the most important thing in the world. Anybody who is anybody in this life always has an education. You have to attend school.'

Cousin Syie turns to me. 'You'll have proper clothes and shoes. We'll pay your lunch money. That will make a big difference to the way you feel about school. There won't be any more times when you go hungry, Johnson. Those days are over. Being hungry can make you feel ill.'

'But I'm not hungry. I eat every day 'cos I work in the kitchens. They feed us in return for the work we do. Doin' stuff with me hands, even if it means doing the washin' up, is better than sittin' in a classroom.'

'There will be no further need to work in the kitchens,' Hammond says.

'Promise me you will give it a try,' Cousin Syie says.

I take a deep breath and nod.

*

We spend the morning going in and out of shops and I come away with T-shirts, shirts that have buttons and long sleeves, shorts, long trousers and Reeboks – shoes that are white and have laces. I pass the time on the journey back learning how to tie a bow on my knee. Hammond is right about something. The clothes and the shoes make me look forward to school. I can't wait to show off my Reeboks.

'Gran!' I burst through the trees and run around her vegetable garden.

I've run all the way and my heart is pounding. She's humming 'Blessed Assurance', the hymn that is always on her lips when she thinks of my grandpa. She opens her arms wide. Even though I know she has had diabetes and high blood pressure, I throw myself into her arms and let her cover me with kisses.

'How's me fav'rit gran'child?' she says, as she squeezes me tight.

'Gran, Gran,' I say, 'you're not goin' to die, are you?'

She laughs. 'I's not goin' anywhere. I's jus' fine.'

There's so much to tell her I don't know where to begin.

'Come on,' she says. 'Let's go an' watch the sun go down.'

We walk around the side of the house together, past the shower that my grandpa made and the bucket in the tree. The sun is already half in the ocean. Between the sunset and my gran and I are the blue-green waves, sea birds riding across the sky, ships steaming to and from St George's, the islands of Carriacou and Petit Martinique – and the smudge on the horizon that is probably St Vincent.

'I missed this,' my gran says.

'Me too,' I say.

'T'ings got worse, but now they better – ain' that right?' she says.

'You won't believe what's happened to me,' I tell her.

'Well,' she says, 'we got all the time in the worl' to talk about it.'

The sun slips below the horizon and my gran gives my shoulders a squeeze. 'Look at the state of me garden,' she says. She has been away for months. The grass is as tall as my knees and there's a lot of fruit that's fallen on the ground.

'I'm sorry, Gran,' I say, 'I shoulda look after it for you.'

'Never min',' she says, and kisses the top of my head. 'We get it lookin' perfec' again in no time.'

She gets to her feet and wanders into the bushes on the edge of her vegetable garden. When she reappears she's clutching a knife in one hand and a large green fruit covered with spines in the other. She sits down beside me and lops off the top of the soursop. Then she pulls two little spoons from the folds of her apron and hands one to me. She doesn't say anything. There is no need. The soursop is my favourite fruit and my gran is back in her little house at the top of the hill. We sit on the steps, the two of us, eating from the same fruit, the sky darkening around us. My gran is right. She always is. Everything has turned out just fine. And we've got all the time in the world.

CHAPTER 11

School is not for me, cars are, but I stick at school to keep my Grand Uncle Hammond happy. But when I'm eleven I get to go and stay with my Uncle Chris and Aunt Jane for two weeks and work with them in their garage. It is the best two weeks of my life, and it goes on, because even after I return to Hammond and Syie's house, Chris lets me go back when I can and work for him: mechanic, paint shop, driver, everything. No matter how suffocated I feel at school, I know that Chris and Jane's garage is only a bus ride away. Soon I'm part of the team. I carry out repairs and help with the spraying. I sit in vehicles under tow and move trucks around the yard. Life is the best it's ever been.

In my last year at the Samaritan Presbyterian, almost all the children who started school with me in Grade 7 move on to secondary education. I take a job as an apprentice panel-beater at a body shop owned by a guy called Kennedy in Sauteurs. Although Kennedy pays me nothing, there are advantages to working for him. I learn quickly and the job is over by lunchtime, leaving me free to make money in other ways – mostly as a carpenter, building cupboards and shelves on local building sites – and at Chris and Jane's garage at weekends. I don't mind putting in the hours, and soon find I'm pocketing more than a hundred dollars a week. A hundred dollars a week in our family – in most families in the village – means rich, but the only thing I spend my wages on is clothes; I don't mean just any old clothes, I mean the best that money in Grenada can buy.

For my family: Jude is working as a cook in St George's and Jill is at home helping to look after Jade, who is now at the Samaritan Presbyterian. All my other brothers and sisters have gone on to school in Sauteurs. My dad hasn't stopped his drinking, but my mum has learned how to live with it.

I'm still with my Grand Uncle Hammond and Cousin Syie, and I always make my visits home when I know my dad isn't going to be around. The only good thing about his drinking and gambling is that I know where he'll be on Friday night – down at the bar at the bottom of the village, blowing his week's earnings.

*

The summer I turn sixteen my world turns upside down. First my cousin Ron is killed and then I get an infection that prevents me from working anywhere near a garage – probably for the rest of my life, if the doctors have their way.

Ron is killed when a boulder the size of a house detaches

itself from a cliff and falls a hundred feet directly on to the bus that he takes to get to work in Sauteurs. His mother, Ena, and his brother and sister, Ali and Nesha, are devastated. We all are.

Weeks later I get a fever, caused by an extreme allergic reaction to the paint used in Chris and Jane's spray shop. The doctors tell me if I go near the place again, it will more than likely kill me.

In the weeks and months after Ron's death, Ena, Nesha and Ali surround themselves with their friends and relatives. There's drink and music as usual, but things aren't the same. I don't think they ever can be. When they close the music down – sometimes at one or two in the morning – Nesha and Ali head for a club called the Arena in Grenville. They're doing their best. They're trying not to do much thinking. Me, I can't stop thinking – thinking about my cousin and the life that I've lost. I try my best to be a part of it all, but I always feel I'm on the outside, looking in.

One night, I'm strolling back to Hammond's after another night killing time, when a beaten-up Honda pulls up in the darkness beside me. The car belongs to a friend of Nesha, a decorator called Lexie who has a gold stud in his nose and gloss paint in his hair. Nesha is in the passenger seat, and three girls, her friends from Victoria, and Ali sit in the back. 'We's goin' to the Arena. D'ya wanna come?'

I look at my watch. It's close to one o'clock in the morning and I'm already heading for a showdown with Hammond. Since Ron's death and the news that I can't go back to work at Chris and Jane's, I've stayed out later and later, breaking my grand uncle's curfew time and time again. Some nights, when the drinking and the talking go on till dawn, I don't even bother to go to bed.

'My brother,' Ali says, 'get in.'

He throws open the door and I squeeze into the back. Grenville is twenty miles away and the road is winding and full of potholes, but we make it there in half an hour because Lexie is a fast driver.

The Arena is a house with a courtyard out the back where there's a tree filled with coloured lights. A guy working a turntable sits behind an upturned crate in a corner, under the open sky. We dance where we can and run for cover when it rains. Tonight the place is packed. I get a Coke from the bar – an old fridge with a big lever handle manned by a guy who keeps change in his hat – and walk outside. One of the girls who came with us, Tania, glances up at me and smiles. I like the beat of the calypso, and I would like to ask her to dance, but I don't want to make a fool of myself, so I stay put, standing on the edge of the courtyard.

Ali turns up with a beer in each hand and stands next to me. He and I take the same bus from the Pool each morning. I get off at Sauteurs and head for Kennedy's garage; he takes another bus to Grenville, where he works as a painter and decorator.

Ali knows Kennedy and Kennedy is mean, he says. Kennedy will do anything to keep me on as an apprentice so he doesn't have to pay me.

'Forget cars,' Ali says. 'You know you can earn good money paintin' and decoratin', 'specially if you good. I seen the way you work, Johnson, the way you build t'ings. There ain' many people in Diego Piece who have what you an' me have. We should team up. Go into business, build our own houses, get rich.'

I smile. When he talks this way he reminds me of Ron.

'T''ink about it,' he says, and thrusts a bottle of beer in my hand. 'But right now, drink this and ask her to dance, my brother.'

I look at the bottle. I'm sixteen years old and I've never let a drop of alcohol pass my lips. I look from the bottle to Tania. Then I look at Ali.

'My brother,' he says, putting his hand on me shoulder, 'it's just a beer.' He clinks his bottle against mine. 'Johnson, you have to loosen up. Take things easy.' He nods in Tania's direction. 'She likes you. But you won't get anywhere by sitting on that bony butt of yours.'

I raise the bottle and drink. It's bitter and cold. I feel it going to work. By my second beer, I start to get used to it. By my third, I actually like it. By my fourth, I'm ready to dance.

CHAPTER 12

Cousin Syie is home with Hammond again after being back in England and she has brought their son Raymond, his wife Irene and my cousins – her grandchildren, Darren and Gavin – with her.

I really like Raymond, Irene and my cousins. Irene is petite and pretty with a bright smile. She works as a nurse in England and dotes on her children; she has a soft spot for me too, maybe because Gavin and I are so alike. After I've helped Hammond prune his orange trees, Irene takes me to one side and asks how I'm doing. She knows I've been hit hard by a chest infection and she has an idea.

'Come and see us in London,' she says. 'Darren and Gavin would love to show you around. You would love it, I know you would. It would do you the world of good to get away. Think about it.'

But I'm having too good a time with Ali, Nesha and the crowd that they hang with to give serious thought to anything else. I've also taken Ali's advice; I'm working less at Kennedy's and more as a painter and decorator.

As the bus bounces along the road to work, Ali asks me

how things worked out with Tania.

'Who?'

'The girl at the Arena. That night we all go in Lexie's car. She liked you and you liked her. Don't you remember, my brother?'

I've danced with so many girls since then and drunk so many beers I struggle to remember anything about that night, or any other. Ali puts his arm on my shoulder.

'Johnson, my brother. Remember what I tell you. Life is for living, but everything in moderation.'

'Sure,' I say.

'Take it easy, my brother.'

The next night I'm sitting on the wall opposite my nan's. Westy and George are passing shots of rum across me to the girls and the girls are pouring them into a jug filled with fruit punch. For the first time in months the boom-box is back on the balcony above Ena's shop. Ena is in the street, swaying to the music, dancing on her own. I watch her, drinking my beer and wondering which of the girls will come with us to the Arena, when my cousin Ansell joins us. He has started bleaching his hair and there are rips in his T-shirt.

He high-fives Joseph, Westy, Mack and George; he's now a full member of their brotherhood. He hardly ever works; his girlfriend brings in the money for the rum he drinks and the weed he smokes, as well as looking after their three kids.

He leans forward.

'Johnson,' he says, 'you lookin' sharp, my brother.'

He gestures to my jeans and trainers. I know he's been drinking long before he got here.

'How many pairs of them trainers you got, brother?'

'Two,' I tell him.

'Your gran' uncle buy 'em for you?'

'No,' I say. 'I bought them myself.'

'Seein' as you got two pairs, then maybe you could see your way to givin' one pair to me, your cousin, who's in need of some shoes right now.'

He laughs, raises his rum glass and clinks it against Westy's.

'How much money you make now, Johnson?' Joseph says.

'That's me own business,' I say.

'Everyt'ing we have here,' Ansell says, 'we ready to share wit' you. Ain' that right, my brothers?'

He nudges George, who produces a bottle and a shot glass from behind the wall.

'I got me a beer,' I say. 'Thanks.'

'Johnson don' drink rum,' Ansell says, leaning forward again so he can catch the attention of the girls. 'He not ready yet to be a man.'

'Leave him alone,' Nesha says. 'He's only just left school.'

I tell her I left school last year. I will be seventeen next month.

'Maybe he don' like the taste,' Mack says. 'How can a

son of the soil not like the taste of pure white rum made an' bottled here in Grenada, from our own sugar cane?'

I've had enough of this.

'I'll take a drink,' I say to George. 'I don't got no problem with rum.'

George passes me two shot glasses. The first he fills with rum, the second with water. Everyone is watching me. I put the glass of rum to my lips.

'Drink her back in one,' Westy says. 'Then chase her down with the water.'

I tell him I know what to do. I expect the rum to burn my mouth and my throat, but it is sweet and cool. It doesn't burn at all.

I put the glass on the wall and wash the rum down with some water. I close my eyes, and start to breathe in through my nose and out through my mouth. The tension and the pressure lift. When I open my eyes again, Westy has refilled the glass. I pick it up and drink.

Me, Ali, Nesha and her friends leave for the Arena at midnight.

The next thing I know, I wake up in my bed, the room spinning. When I close my eyes the sickness rushes like a wave from my head to my belly. Pictures flash in front of my eyes: the striped label of a bottle of white rum; the winding road from Diego Piece; lights pulsing at the Arena.

I manage to clamp my hand to my mouth as the vomit shoots up my throat. It seeps into my nose and through my fingers. I make a lunge for the door, but as I open it I throw up on the floor.

My grand uncle is standing across the corridor. For a moment our eyes meet, then I run as fast as I can to the toilet. I don't have the strength to close the door behind me. I fall forward and spew my guts into the bowl.

CHAPTER 13

Two nights later, I'm leaving the house to go to Ena's when I run into Hammond on the drive. He's carrying a basket full of oranges, bananas and plums. Since Syie, Raymond, Irene, Darren and Gavin went back to England he has spent all his spare time in the grove behind the house. He even takes a torch up there and tends to his trees in the dark.

I leave the back door open for him and the light from inside the house shines on his face.

'Where are you going?' he asks.

'Out,' I reply.

He looks at me with his big, sad eyes. 'Where did we go wrong, Syie and me?'

'I don't know what you talking about,' I tell him.

'What more could you want, that we haven't already given you?'

I don't need this right now, I say to myself, and carry on walking towards the gate.

'Enough of this,' Hammond says. 'Look at me, Johnson, when I'm talking to you.'

The sharpness in his voice, something I've never heard

before, stops me in my tracks. I turn.

'You're staying in tonight,' he says. 'No more of this. You're shaming yourself. You're shaming your family. And you're shaming me.'

'Shame?' I say. 'Where's the shame in what I do?'

'The drinking, the girls, the partying, Johnson. It has to stop.'

I tell him I'm not a child. I'm no longer at school. I'm making my own way now.

'While you live in this house,' he says, 'you will obey my rules.'

'Then it's simple,' I tell him. 'I'll no longer live in this house.'

I turn and walk down the drive. I open the gate, step into the road and glance back through the wrought-iron bars. My grand uncle is standing in the light from the back door, his two dogs at his feet, his shoulders slumped. Our eyes meet and the look on his face takes the sting out of my anger. Hammond is alone now – Syie will be in England for several more months.

I turn my back on the house, knowing that Grand Uncle Hammond is still watching me.

One of the dogs lets out a low howl. I feel ashamed, but I can't turn back. The air is thick and damp and filled with the sound of crickets.

I head up the hill. TV screens flicker in darkened rooms

on either side of me. I smell roasting meat, spices, breadfruit, bananas and coconut milk; I hear music and laughter. The guys are cooking oil-down – chicken, dumplings, breadfruit and coconut milk - on an open fire on the corner by the standpipe.

Westy, George, Mack, Joseph and Ansell have been there, as usual, since the early afternoon. Ansell holds a piece of meat on the end of his knife and turns it in the flames.

'You want to stop and eat? We get us some manicou today,' Joseph says.

Manicou is like a possum.

I thank him, but move on. I reach the pathway that leads to our house. I brush past the noni tree. The smell of rancid cheese from its fruit hangs heavily in the air. There's laughter inside.

Jeffon and Jade chase each other between the rooms. I realize how much I miss them. The way they're playing tells me my father is not back. I pull back the door and step inside. Jeffon and Jade stop their chasing game and stare at the person who has walked through the door. Then Jade's face breaks into a big smile.

'Johnson!'

He throws himself at me. The others rush over too.

It's good to be home again.

CHAPTER 14

A three-quarter moon shines through the window above my head. I know that my father will be working himself into a fury as he weaves his way up the hill. I switch the radio off and listen. I no longer hear my mother. My father must not know that she has been crying. Seeing the misery he causes just makes things worse.

The little bed groans under my weight. She might have supported me perfectly when I was nine, but she struggles now. It's hard to believe she has survived all these years. I hear the dogs barking. I count the seconds, a cold feeling in my stomach. A shout. My father is abusing our neighbour, a nice man in his sixties, out on his balcony enjoying a quiet drink.

There's a loud crash as my dad kicks in our front door. To get to the main bedroom – where my mother is waiting – he must go through ours. I roll over, my heart in my throat. My father is still on the porch. He hurls a final string of insults at the man next door. The walls of the house are so thin he could already be in the room with us. Jade sits bolt upright in bed. I don't know if he's awake or dreaming, but he starts to cry.

I hear a voice telling my father to shut up. It takes me a moment to realize it belongs to me. There's a terrible silence, the kind of silence that comes between lightning and thunder. Then, with a roar of rage, my father bursts into the room, nearly wrenching the door from its hinges. The moonlight is strong enough for me to see him clearly – and for him to see us.

Something glints in his right hand. An empty bottle falls to the ground and smashes into tiny pieces. My father steps into the room and trips on the corner of the little bed. He falls headlong towards me. The frame collapses and I scramble out of the way. He catches sight of the radio. He grabs it, raises himself off the ground and hurls it out of the window. I'm in the corner, next to the big bed. My brothers and sisters are sitting rigid, their backs against the wall. Jeffon has clamped his hand over Jade's mouth.

To get to me, my father must launch himself across the bed. I don't like to think about what will happen if my brothers and sisters get in his way. I run towards him, wait for him to lunge at me, then duck. I feel the swish of his arm as he grabs for me and misses. I'm where I want to be – by the door. I hardly notice the stabbing pain in my heel as I step on the broken glass.

My father stares at me and I stare at him. I turn and run, hoping he will follow. I don't know where I'm going, just that

I need to be far away. If I go, maybe his anger will go too, and the rest of them will be safe. Before I make my move, my father bends and picks up what's left of the little bed. There's a splintering sound as he pulls it from the wall. He lifts the bed above his head and hurls it out of the window as well.

I turn and run. He crashes after me, but only gets as far as the balcony before he trips and falls.

I rush past the nutmeg tree and into the bushes. There I lie down in a hollow behind the saffron, my heart beating against my chest. A few minutes later I hear my mother calling my name. The sound is soft and haunting and I want so much to go towards it. It cuts me like a knife to hear her say my name over and over. But I stay where I am, perfectly still. I can't go back. When I do, something bad always happens. It's better I stay away.

It's between five-thirty and six when I reach my gran's place. She's sitting where she usually sits, on a large rock in front of her house, singing to herself. When I get a little closer she stops and smiles.

'Are you going to speak about it, then?'

Her eyebrows narrow, wrinkling her forehead.

'About what, Gran?'

'No use hidin' it. Somet'ing has happen. An' now you goin' to speak about it.'

Maybe she heard something during the night, or maybe it's written on my face. Somehow my gran always knows when something is wrong. I tell her what happened.

I tell her about my bad behaviour to Hammond; I tell her about my anger and shame at having to run from my own home. The words nearly choke me, but I try to hold my head high and fix my gaze on the place where the jungle meets the sky.

'I will never run away again, Gran,' I say. 'Never. Not from anyone, or anything.'

My gran listens, her eyes closed, her face turned towards the sun as it slowly rises above the hills. When I finish she opens them again and stares out over the village. There's a look on her face that is happy and sad at the same time. It's the look she gives me whenever she has seen my grandfather. Her eyes shine.

'Is this how you want to end up?' she says. 'Don't think I don't know what you do, runnin' around with them cousins an' friends, smokin' and drinkin' and wastin' all you money down at them clubs. Do you want to end up like him?'

She gestures at the jumble of planks and galvanized that makes up our house.

'I don't smoke that stuff, Gran. Never have,' I tell her truthfully.

Plenty of my friends do, of course, and I've seen what it does to them; I never like to lose that much control. But I've no answer for her on the drinking and she knows it.

'Me dad and me are two completely different people,'

I say, staring at my feet.

My gran laughs. I look up. The sadness is still in her eyes.

'You know why he drink?' she says. 'You know what's eatin' at him?'

I say nothing. I'm not sure I want to hear what she is going to tell me.

'You father work hard all he life. An' for what?' she says. 'He see what you Gran' Uncle Hammond do for heself and know he could have achieved all them same t'ings. He angry with the way he life turn out. An' now it too late to change it. It eat an' eat away at him. Is that how you want to be?'

'I'm never going to be like my dad,' I tell her.

'Well, this is how it start,' she replies. Her voice softens. 'When you was little, playin' in the roots of that tree, sometimes I look at you and I call you Michael, 'cos I forget – I t'ink it you dad, not you. But you an' him is different, Johnson. Every time you make somet'ing, every time you build somet'ing wit' you hands, you make an idea in you head come real. You make it happen. You father, when he your age, he have all them same ideas, but he never act on them. He don' know how to. An that when he turn to drinkin.'

'But why does he hate me, Gran?'

My gran sighs.

'He don' hate you. He love you, Johnson. It's heself that he can' stand the sight of.' She turns and touches my face. 'You a good child – you smart, kind an' good. Do somet'ing with you life, Johnson. Don't throw it all away.'

I tell her I'm not sure where to begin.

'No more drinking,' she says. 'No more late nights, apologize to your grand uncle and come and live with me. You t'ink you can do that?'

I smile.

'What choices do I have?' I ask her.

'People always has choices,' she says. She smiles again. 'You'll know what they are right enough when the time come.'

CHAPTER 15

And so I move in with my gran. Life is good. Work is good.

Meryl Scott, my mother's cousin, and her husband, Neville, ask me to fit out their new house with built-in cupboards and then paint the place from top to bottom. Like Hammond and Syie, Meryl and Neville have spent most of their adult lives in the UK and come back to Grenada to retire. The house they've built is not quite as big as Hammond's, but big enough. They want the work done quickly and the deal is worth a small fortune. They've seen me work; they've spoken to my grand uncle and know that I will get the job done on time and do it well. Shannon, an old school friend, is going to help me.

Around the same time I start to date a girl who lives with her family in a village down the road from Diego Piece. I build myself a bicycle from two broken bikes that I buy for scrap. She's not a Porsche 911 Turbo, but she's good enough and I cycle to see my girlfriend after I finish work. I like her family very much, especially her grandad, who is full of talk about his days as a soldier during the Second World War. I've heard stories of German submarines surfacing off the coast by Point Ross, though I've never really taken them seriously. But, real or not, these kinds of stories made a lot of Grenadians focus on the war and ask themselves what they could do to help Britain fight.

As we sit out on the balcony and talk, I envy him his experience. He never saw action, but his army service was clearly the moment his life changed.

'Any chance you get to travel,' he tells me, 'you have to seize it. This is what the army gave me. A chance to see something of the world.' He smiles and raises his glass – and from the far-off look in his eyes I know he's thinking of old soldiers, old friends. 'God is a Grenadian,' he says, then knocks back his drink.

I say maybe I should join the army and my girlfriend's mother starts to laugh. 'With dreadlocks that hang past you shoulders, the idea of being in anyone's army is pretty funny,' she says.

After sunset I cycle back to Diego Piece. I never much liked the dark and there are places on the journey that still scare me, even now. It's close to midnight, but the air is warm. I feel something in the air. It's like my gran says: something ain' right.

As I carry on up the hill I sense somebody waiting just beyond the bridge. I start talking to myself. Come on, Johnson, you ain' a kid no more, you nineteen, for God's sake . . . But unlike my gran's, my eyes are perfect. The figure is still there and it's waving at me. I pick up a rock from the side of the road, grit my teeth and walk on, pushing the bike.

A few feet nearer and the hand that's waving at me changes into a banana leaf moving in the breeze. I'm so relieved I put my bike down, sit beside the road and laugh. I tell myself that I'm a stupid, superstitious fool. I pick up my bike and continue on foot. I'm fifty metres beyond the bridge, when I hear a sound behind me – the sound of a shoe scraping on the road. This time it's real.

I whip around and see someone emerging from the shadow of a house.

'Who is it? Who's there?'

'Relax, cousin.'

As he moves away from the wall, the moonlight picks out Ansell's tight bleached curls.

'Been someplace nice, cousin?'

I've been someplace, I tell him.

'On that?'

He points to the bike.

It works good, I tell him. I made it myself.

'Course,' he says. 'You make every'ting youself, don' you, Johnson? You doin' OK, ain' that right? I's surprise you don' have a car a'ready wit' all that money you makin'.'

'What's on you mind, Ansell? It's late, and I'm ready for me bed.'

'Me an' some of the brothers been wantin' to speak to you

for a while,' he says. 'It about this work that you do . . .'

'What about it?'

'There a lot of people in Deego Pee who'd like that contrac'. A lot of people that don't t'ink it right so much work should go to two people.'

I want to point out that Ansell has never done a day's work in his life, but I tell him instead that I got the deal fair and square.

'If you say so, cousin. But I t'ink you understand what I sayin'.'

'No, I don't,' I say.

'It would be nice – a nice gesture – if you give some of you brothers some of the money you makin'. The money go a long way to ironin' out the ill feelin' that exists wit' some of them. After all, you know that what we got we always happy to share wit' you . . .'

In the moonlight, I can see that he's holding up a bottle.

'No thanks,' I tell him.

I turn and start walking up the hill.

'Johnson!' His sharp tone makes me stop. 'I ain' done talkin' wit' you.'

'What is it you want, Ansell? You want money? Is that what you askin' from me?'

'Give it to me an' I see it get to the right people,' he says.

I see something glint low down by his waist. He has a knife in his other hand.

'You t'ink you better than we – is that right, cousin?'

'I work hard for me money, Ansell,' I say.

'Then share a little, brother.'

'No,' I say, and carry on up the hill.

As I walk, the goosebumps come right back. I strain to hear the slightest sound that Ansell is following me, but when I reach the corner and look back, he's gone.

CHAPTER 16

I'm putting the finishing touches to a cupboard in Meryl and Neville's bedroom, when there's a sharp knock on the door. They are not in and Shannon is in the basement painting the kitchen. I open the front door and there is my mother.

She's crying and my first thought is that this is about my father. But it's nothing to do with him. It's about what happened last night. There are people in the village who are out to get me. She's terrified that something bad is going to happen to me. My poor mum is shaking. I take her by the hand.

'Nothing goin' to happen. You got enough worries without having to think of me. Go home. I'm fine.'

I squeeze her hand.

'I'm scared, Johnson. I ain' never hear people talk this way before.'

'They full of envy, Mummy. That all this is about.'

'If it about the money, Johnson, then give them what they want. Just give it. Hand it over. Nothing worth this pain.'

I shake my head and put a finger to my lips.

'Mummy, quiet, don't vex yourself like this. It not about

the money. This is about something else, something I feel real strong about.'

She wipes the tears from her eyes with her sleeve.

'They want money for nothing and that not right,' I say. 'What me gran always say?'

'Love, respect, honesty.'

I nod my head.

'All me life I work hard, Mummy. I never been afraid of hard work. If Ansell don't want to work, then that he business. But he ain' never going to take me money for sitting on he backside and doing nothing.'

My mother takes a deep breath and says slowly, 'God knows, I seen wha' happen to me sister when the Good Lord take she two sons from her. I seen what it do to her, Johnson. Do you want to do the same t'ing to me? Listen to me. The way they talkin', they's goin' to kill you.'

I pull her to me and wrap her in my arms.

'Go home, Mummy. Nobody going to get killed. Nobody. I promise. Go home.'

'What you goin' to do?' she says.

'I don' know. I talk to Shannon about it. He got a good head on him. Shannon and me talk it through.' I kiss her on the head. 'Go.'

I watch her walk up the hill, back to our house. I close the door behind me and set off down the road. Everybody I expect to see is by Ena's house, either sitting on the wall or standing in the street. The fire is going and Mack is fanning the flames with a banana leaf. Joseph has a small transistor radio to his ear. George is plucking a chicken. He has feathers all over his lap. Westy is holding a bottle of rum up to the light, seeing how much is left before he cracks open another. Ansell is sitting next to him. There's something in his hand. At first I think it's a knife, but then I realize it's a piece of broken mirror. He's holding it up to his face and trimming his hair with a pair of scissors.

He pushes himself off the wall, the scissors in his right hand, the broken mirror in his left.

'Stay away from me and stay away from me family,' I tell him.

I manage to keep myself from shouting, but he sees I'm angry.

'Easy, cousin.'

The commotion makes the others stop what they're doing. George stands up in a cloud of feathers. Joseph puts his radio down.

'Johnson, be cool, my brother. Stop an' have some oildown wit' us,' he says.

I keep my eyes on Ansell.

'I will never give you a cent of any money I make, is that clear?' I say to him.

'No call for that kinda talk, cousin,' Ansell says. 'No call at all.'

'If you have a problem with what I do, Ansell, you talk to me about it. If I see any fear in my mum's eyes on account of you, I'll kill you, is that clear?'

'Easy, cousin. Don' disrespec' me now.'

'How can I disrespect you?' I tell him.

Mack steps forward. He has a beer in his hand. It's a peace offering, and as I look at him I take my eyes off Ansell.

Ansell seizes the moment. I duck and feel the swish of his arm as the scissors miss my head by a fraction of an inch. I pull back my fist and drive it into his face with all the anger in my belly.

He topples backwards over the wall, knocking down the bottle of rum as he goes.

I turn and walk away.

'You's dead,' the voice shouts after me. 'Dead, you hear? You's a worthless piece, Johnson Beharry. You never fit in this village. You don't fit on this islan'. You don't fit, you don' fit . . .'

He pauses to spit the blood from his lip on to the road.

I keep walking, my eyes on the point where the land meets the sky.

'You don't fit, you hear? You never have ...' The words ring in my head. 'Even you own family don't want you. You own family t'ink you's a piece of rubbish too ... You's dead, Johnson. Dead.'

I need to get away. It's like my mum says: there's trouble in the air. People don't trust me. I see it in their eyes everywhere I go. I'm the guy who won't share the money he's making with people who need it. I'm the guy who lost it with Ansell. I'm the troublemaker. I'm Michael Bolah's son. I'm the guy who don't fit . . .

My mother is angry. I told her I wouldn't make trouble; I told her I would calm the situation down. Instead I've made it worse. My father is out on the porch drinking. Have I brought this on? I don't know. But I know the warning signs. It's best to stay away. But where to go?

Then it hits me: England. To London. I've got an aunt and uncle over there – Raymond's my grand uncle's son and Irene is his wife. Irene says any time I want to come over, I can. My cousins Gavin and Darren too. So that's what I'm going to do. I'm going to go to England for a holiday. I'm going to go and stay with my Uncle Raymond and Auntie Irene.

CHAPTER 17

The following day I go and see Grand Uncle Hammond. If anyone understands my wish to go to England, it's him. I find him in the nutmeg grove above the house. He's halfway up a stepladder, pruning the branches of a big, healthy tree that will bring him a lot of fruit when it comes to the harvest next year. I can see the ladder swaying.

I tell him, Stop, I'll do it for you, and pull myself up into the tree. Hammond passes me the clippers and I set about trimming the upper branches. As I work, with him directing me, I tell him my plan.

'Are you sure this is what you want to do?' he asks.

'Quite sure,' I tell him.

'England isn't like Grenada.'

'I know. That's why I want to go.'

'It can be cold and lonely. The English can be cold too.'

'I'm just going for a holiday, Grand Uncle. They get a summer in England too, don't they?'

'Some call it a summer.'

Hammond says I can use his phone to call Irene and Raymond.

Irene is thrilled.

'When will you be here?'

'I've got to finish the job I'm working on. It will probably take me another week. I plan on coming for a month. Is that all right? Can I really stay?'

'Johnson, our home is yours, you know that,' she tells me. 'We've got room downstairs, if you don't mind sleeping on the settee. I can't wait to tell Darren and Gavin. They'll be so excited. There's so much to see here. They can show you all the sights.'

Two days later I catch a bus to St George's and book my ticket. I have enough money to pay the deposit, but the travel agent will need the balance before I fly. I take a deep breath. I'm cutting things fine. I've told Irene that I'm arriving on 7 August, but it will be touch-and-go whether I finish my painting job by then. But I've no problem with Shannon completing the contract – he's a good decorator and I trust him. It's how I get the money in time to pay for the ticket that's vexing me. I see no way around it until my nan loans me the five hundred dollars I need. I arrange for Shannon to pay her back as soon as he finishes the house. My mother is happy because she believes that my being away for four weeks will calm things down with Ansell and the others. And she knows I'll be in good hands in London.

*

During the rest of the week I tie up loose ends. I say goodbye to my mum, my brothers and sisters and to Hammond. On my very last night, after I finish work, I stop by Old Man Baptiste's. I find him out the front of his house with a group of workers who are about to go into his plantation for a night of harvesting by torchlight. He's older, thinner and shorter than the day he handed me a pair of shiny red and white flip-flops, but the look he gives me is the same. Old Man Baptiste will go to his grave with one eyebrow cocked higher than the other. He still trusts nobody.

'What do you want, Beharry?'

'I've come to buy something from you,' I tell him.

'What is it that you want to buy from me?'

'A coconut tree. A little one.'

'A coconut tree? What in God's name do you want with a coconut tree? Are you making one of your damn contraptions again?'

I shake my head.

'If there's somewhere you been, a place where you lived where you been happy, you plant a tree in that place. It's a kind of a … tradition.'

'Beharry, I don't have time for tradition. I'm a busy man, as you can see.'

'I know. So I'll take the tree now if you'll sell it to me.'

He barks orders to his foreman. Time is moving on and there's fruit to be picked. He wants to make a start before it gets dark.

I follow Old Man Baptiste to the back of his house. I expect him to send me with one of his servants to a field here he has hundreds of coconut trees, but we climb the steps to his terrace. Here he keeps a large number of pots with plants of all colours and sizes. It's a small piece of paradise and it surprises me. He waves at a pot in the corner and tells me to take it. It's mine.

'But these are you own trees,' I say.

'Sure. So what? Trees are trees. Plenty more where they came from. And I don't want any of your damn money either.'

'I don't know what to say, Mr Baptiste. Thank you.'

I pick up the pot and turn to go.

'Beharry,' he says.

I look at him.

'I heard what happened down in the village.'

I say nothing.

'It took guts to do what you did. The tree is a token of . . . my appreciation.' He sticks out his hand. 'Truce?'

I smile.

'Mr Baptiste, there been a truce between us now for a long, long time.'

'Well, just see that it stays that way,' he says.

He heads down the steps and disappears.

*

When I present my gran with the tree she starts to thank me but I hear the catch in her voice that she gets at moments like these and we end up, as we often do, in silence, on the steps, gazing out over the village and the mountains.

After supper we go into the garden to find a place to plant the tree.

'Here,' she says at long last. 'We plant it in the vegetable patch. I be able to see her every day when I come an' pick me veg an' fruit.'

'Gran, I'm just goin' away for a few weeks.'

She says nothing. The silence between us is so thick I'd need a machete to cut it.

'Gran, what is it?'

'I been dreamin' again,' she says. 'Dreamin' 'bout you.'

'A good dream or a bad dream?'

'I dream 'bout you a lot, Johnson. An' always it the same dream. I dream you walkin' along the road from Sauteurs to Deego Pee. I know the road, I see him, but he differen' from normal. There's all kindsa blockage – a boulder, galvanized, a dead cow, broken-down cars . . . so much blockage in the road. But you take no notice, you just climb over it or walk roun' it an' in the end you get to where you goin'.'

'That's good, then, isn't it?' I say.

'Yes,' she says, 'that's good.'

'But what does it mean?' I ask.

'It mean a lot of things,' she says. 'It mean you growin' up.

It mean you won't be needin' you old gran so much as you used to need her.'

'You talk like I ain' never comin' back, Gran.'

'You ain',' she says. 'Not for a long time.'

'Gran, it's just a holiday.'

She shakes her head.

'You gran is right,' she says, 'always is.' She touches my face. I've never seen my gran crying before, but she's crying now. She's crying because it's almost dark and she thinks, with her bad eyes, that because she can't see me I can't see her.

'Now come along,' she says, suddenly, 'an' plan' this tree wit' me before she get so dark I trip an' break me bones.'

I get a little spade that she keeps in the house and I dig a hole half a metre deep. I pull the sapling from the pot and am about to drop it into the hole, when she stops me.

'How long before you get a coconut on a coconut tree?'

I reply that it's four, maybe five years.

She nods.

Did I know, she says, that if you sit down while you plant a tree, it bears fruit a whole lot quicker?

I shake my head.

'Help me to sit down,' she says.

And so we sit, the two of us, side by side, up to our wrists in the damp soil, patting it down, and though I see no sign of my grandpa, I certainly feel him, and I guess that my gran does too, because she starts to hum and when she's done with humming, she begins to sing: 'This is my story, this is my song, Praising my Saviour all the day long. Angels descending bring from above Echoes of mercy, whispers of love ...'

CHAPTER 18

I'm sitting in a window seat, trying to get a look at England as the plane goes down, but we're in cloud. I can see nothing.

The air conditioning is cold on my skin – I'm wearing jeans and a T-shirt with the green, yellow and orange of the Grenadian flag on it – and I'm looking forward to the moment when we land so I can warm up again. I hope Raymond and Irene are there to meet me. I left messages on their answering machine with details of my flight and arrival, but I never got a reply. I don't even have their address.

Once we've landed, I make for a big hall filled with people. There are neon signs everywhere, pointing to 'Taxis', 'Buses' and 'Car Parks'. I'm standing staring at them, wondering which way to go, people pushing past me, when I hear someone call my name. I turn and there's my cousin Gavin.

'Hey,' he says and we embrace.

Another shout, and Darren, Raymond and Irene rush up and greet me.

'Hammond gave us your flight details,' Irene says.

'You didn't get me messages?'

She shakes her head.

'Not your fault. Our answering machine's been playing up. Raymond called Hammond and Hammond got them from Jemeela.' She gives me a hug. 'Where are your bags?'

'I don't have no bags, except for this.' I point to the rucksack on my back.

'Oh, Johnson,' she says. 'You're going to freeze half to death.'

'They told me it was summer,' I tell her.

'Yes, Sweetie,' she says. 'But it ain' like Grenada. Not one little bit.'

*

London started out as a holiday for me, a place to take a break from what was going on back home, but before I know it I'm living here properly. I go to college to study motor mechanics, which means my visa gets extended. The trouble is, I already know all the stuff the teacher is telling us. Like when we get a lecture on electrical circuits, I have to bite my tongue to stop myself telling the teacher I know everything I need about electrical circuits already – and if he needs the proof, all he has to do is come and take a look at Raymond and Irene's house, where I've just rewired the whole top floor.

Gavin and Darren know some guys who work on a building site in west London, and within a couple of weeks I'm employed for as much time as I can spare. To start with I work for two days a week, but as time goes on I do more. The money is good and the work is varied and I don't need much of an excuse to dodge the classroom.

After months of jobbing around, moving wherever I'm sent, I end up working on a huge building project in northwest London and start to fall into a routine. The days I work on the site, I get up at six, catch the tube, arrive at work by eight and stay till around four. Soon I'm pocketing close to £1500 a month.

It's not long before I drop out of college completely and work full-time instead. Irene is disappointed, of course. But when we sit down and talk about it she agrees there's no point in throwing good money at something I really can't stand. The work is good and so, for the moment at least, I plan on staying.

I'm earning a small fortune by Grenadian standards, but after paying back my tuition fees and giving something every week to Irene and Raymond for my board and lodging, my money goes as fast as I earn it.

What Irene, Raymond, Darren and Gavin don't know is that I'm spending most of my spare time and money with a new pal, Keely, and another mate, Abs, and our life is party, party, party. Only I know how badly my life is spiralling out of control; and this time I don't know how to stop it.

One evening Keely invites me around to a friend's place. It's not far. The idea is to grab a takeaway pizza, have a few drinks, then go out clubbing.

I get home after work, change and call him on my mobile to find out where they all are. He gives me an address that turns out to be within walking distance and ten minutes later I'm ringing the bell. The door is opened by an Asian guy dripping with jewellery, topped off by a short fringe that's plastered on to his forehead with buckets of gel.

He throws an arm around me and ushers me into the lounge. The air is thick with smoke. The smell takes me straight back to Diego Piece. If I were to close my eyes I would see Ansell, Mack, Joseph, Westy and George. Instead, through the haze, I see Keely and Abs. They wave to me.

There are four unopened pizza boxes on the table. Among the glasses I also spot a bottle of rum. An expensive-looking sound system fills the room with a low, pulsing beat.

'Hey, Johnson, my brother,' Keely says.

The guy with the gold tooth still has his arm around my shoulders.

'You know each other?' Keely asks him.

'Sure,' the Asian says, turning to me and holding out his arm. 'The name's Aziz.'

I look at his hand.

'Hey, it ain' gonna bite ya.' He sniggers.

Keely and Abs laugh too.

'Keely, Absy and me is old friends,' Aziz says. He's still holding his hand out. 'Any friend of Keely an' Absy is a friend of mine. How about a drink?'

He puts his hand in mine and we shake, hands clasped, brother-style, like we're about to arm-wrestle.

'That's more like it. You live pretty close, I hear.'

'Yeah, not far,' I say.

I'm careful not to tell him more.

He reaches for the bottle.

'How do you like your rum?'

Straight, I tell him, with a glass of water to chase.

'The only way,' he says approvingly.

He pours out four shots and hands them around.

'To new friends,' he says.

We chink glasses and wash down the drinks in one. Aziz is quick to pour me another. By the time I've had three, I start to relax.

The joint comes around the table and everyone is taking hits. Even when I was partying back in Diego Piece I never smoked. Here it seems to go with the territory. I take a pull, sucking the smoke down. For a second I think my head is going to explode, then I let fly and hack the smoke back into the room.

'Whoa,' Aziz says, patting me on the back, 'someone's out of practice here.'

The next time the joint comes round, I know everyone is looking at me. This time the smoke goes down and it stays down.

I pass the joint along. The rest of that night is not too clear.

*

By six in the morning everyone is on the point of passing out. Keely says I can stay, but I tell him I'm only just down the road and I might as well go home. Aziz staggers to his feet as I get to mine.

'Hey, Bro,' he says, 'we must do this again sometime. Now I know where you hang, I'll catch you down the pub. Till next time, yeah?'

I step out into the dawn. Spring is supposed to be here, but the air is still freezing. For once I'm thankful for the rain. It feels cool on my face.

I need to sober up. I suck in a great lungful of air.

When I reach the end of the street, I turn to check I'm not being followed, then quicken my pace. Ten minutes later I reach the house.

I fumble with the keys and step into the hallway. I walk through to the kitchen, where I pour myself a glass of water and sit down at the table in the darkness. As I drink, I think of my gran. I think back to the last time I saw her, how we planted the coconut tree together, and I remember what she told me.

I thought I was coming to England for a holiday; I told

her I'd be coming back. But my gran knew.

You won't be coming back for a long time, she said. She was right. Is this what she saw? I'm never going to be like my dad, I told her. Yet, here I am, hanging out with Keely, Abs and Aziz; drinking and smoking myself senseless. This is how it starts, she said, this is how it all starts…

I drink another glass of water and go into the sitting room. I want to be in bed before Irene gets back from her nightshift. I don't want to look into her eyes when she walks through the door. And I don't want her to look into mine.

CHAPTER 19

For the next few weeks I do my best to keep myself straight. I am not my father, I tell myself. I stay away from the places where I'm likely to bump into Keely and Abs.

Then one day I get back in the evening and hear a rap on the door. Irene is already out on her rounds. Raymond is watching TV. Darren and Gavin are still at work. I open the door and find Keely, Abs and Aziz on the doorstep.

'Hey, JB, how's things?' Aziz says. 'I hope you don't mind us dropping by?'

'I … no,' I stammer.

'We ain't seen you down the pub in a while,' Keely says.

'Wondered what had happened to you,' Abs adds.

'You look surprised, man,' Aziz says.

'I didn't realize you knew where I lived,' I say.

'Got your address from Cameron, didn't we?' Keely says. 'You were legless one night. Cameron ordered you a taxi. You gave him your address. Ring any bells?'

Inside, a part of me is dying. I do now remember staggering out of a taxi after a heavy night at the pub. I must have given the barman my address when he called the cab company.

'You going to ask us in, mate? It's getting cold out here.'

I have to think on my feet. I tell him I'd like to, but I can't – it's my aunt and uncle's place and they're expecting guests. It's a family occasion. I roll my eyes. You know how it is. Gotta be on my best behaviour …

As I watch them go, Raymond calls out from the sitting room. He wants to know who was at the front door. Nobody much, I tell him. If Raymond saw Aziz, Keely and Abs, he'd have a heart attack.

How am I going to deal with this?

A couple of days slip by. I go to work. I start to hear the tick of a clock. Any moment now Aziz, Keely and Abs are going to come looking for me. God, what am I going to do?

On the last day of the working week I'm on the Tube, on my way to work, reading a newspaper someone's left on the seat next to me, when I spot something – a recruiting ad for the British Army. I read it and flick on to the next page. But something about it pulls me back. Recruits don't have to be British to apply; foreign and Commonwealth applicants will be considered on their merits.

Once the idea gets a hold inside my head, I can't shake it. Grenada is a former British colony, so I'm eligible. If I joined the army it would solve my problems at a stroke. I can remain in the UK. I might even get a British passport. I'll also get a reasonable wage, but best of all, I'll break completely with the past.

As I walk on to the building site, I feel like I'm on a mission. It's like a light's gone on. Joining the army. It's the solution to all my problems.

*

I call in at the pub on the way home from work. Keely and Abs are there, and Aziz turns up after Keely calls him on the mobile. I tell them I've made a big decision and I want them to be the first to know.

At first they think I'm kidding. The mood only turns serious when they see I'm not going along with their backslapping and high-fiving.

'The army is seriously racist,' Aziz says. 'You won't last a minute. What planet is you on, man?'

'Yeah, the army is the same as the cops, they treats black people real bad,' Keely says. 'Don't do it. You're in a good job, earning good money. Why blow it, Bro?'

'And we'd never see you again!' Aziz flashes his gold-tooth smile.

'Ol' Aziz is always right. You'll be stuck in some dump on the far side of the world, dishin' out parking tickets. Don't do it, man. Stay here.'

He doesn't realize it, but this is the best reason I've heard yet for giving it a go.

The person who nearly derails me is Irene. She knows nothing of the people I've been hanging with, the rubbish I've been smoking and how much I hate myself for doing it. For a year and a half she and Raymond have made me as much a part of their lives as their own children. In return I've betrayed their trust, and the trust of everyone I love in Grenada. Just distancing myself from Aziz, Abs, Keely and co. is not going to work. It's not just them; it's everything.

In Grenada I was just messing about. Here I can feel myself sinking.

I think of my dad. I have to start again. I have to make something of my life.

CHAPTER 20

The next day I leave work early and head over to Wembley, not far from the stadium. The recruiting centre looks more like a shop than an office and I wonder how its plate-glass window is still there – the newsagent and off-licence on either side are protected by serious amounts of heavy wire mesh.

'Hi,' I say, 'I'm interested in joining the army.'

The sergeant asks if it would be helpful to talk to another Grenadian who's been in the army a while and who can tell me about army life. He leads me into the next room and I'm amazed to see someone I already know. I met Jeremy Forrester, another Grenadian, on a building site in London around a year ago. Then I moved on to other jobs and lost touch. I had no idea he'd joined the army.

'How does it work?' I ask him.

'OK. We get you to come back and do a theory test. It's pretty basic – they're not looking for people with university degrees. You just have to demonstrate you can read and write and do a bit of multiplication. You can do the British Army Recruit Battery test as early as next week.'

'What's that?'

'It's common sense, basically. Pass that and you'll go down to Pirbright, where they'll put you through two days of leadership and teamwork exercises, plus they'll see if you're up to it physically. At the end of the two days, provided you're still with the programme, they'll interview you. Tell them the kind of unit you want to be in and how joining up is something you've given a lot of thought to.'

'What kind of unit do I want to join?' I ask.

'Well, in terms of the front line, there's the cavalry and the infantry. In the cavalry – we're talking tanks, basically – there are eleven armoured regiments and one mounted ceremonial regiment. I'm infantry. The Princesses of Wales' Royal Regiment: the PWRR.'

'Then that's what I want to be in. If it's good enough for you, it's good enough for me.'

The 1st Battalion PWRR, the one Jeremy's in, is set to deploy to Kosovo in March of next year, roughly a month after my training ends.

A week later I return to the recruiting centre for two formal interviews and the BARB test. I sit down at a computer terminal and get fed a series of questions designed to assess my reasoning, my use of English and my mental arithmetic. The questions are easy: 'High is to low, as full is to what?' You have to pick one of three choices. Or, 'Which number comes next in the following sequence: one, two, four, eight …?'

I pass the test easily and they give me a pamphlet about the infantry and the PWRR, which I'm to read before I head down to Pirbright, near Aldershot, for two days of assessment.

I arrive a week later, undergo a full medical, pass that, get a series of briefs about army life, march around a parade ground and eat my first meal at a NAAFI.

Throughout this time, recruiting personnel watch your every move – assessing your character as well as your ability to get on with others.

The next morning we are sent on a mile-and-a-half run. You're supposed to complete this in no more than ten minutes and thirty seconds. I do it in less than eight.

After some strength tests – lifting a few weights in a gym – we're divided into groups and set a series of initiative tests designed to see whether we can solve specific challenges while working in teams. This is the bit I like best of all, as you're given a plank, an oil drum, a couple of poles, a rope and a pulley, and have to use them to get you and your team across an imaginary stream.

Finally I'm interviewed by an officer, a major. He's sitting behind a desk and barely looks up as I enter the room. I haven't been nervous before, but I am now. This is it. When I leave this room I will know whether I've passed or failed.

He starts by asking whether I've encountered any particular problems during the selection process and I tell him, no, none.

'So you want to join the infantry?'

'Yes, sir.'

'Do you know the role of the infantry?'

I tell him that the infantry has peacekeeping and humanitarian roles, in addition to a war-fighting responsibility, and that it can be sent almost anywhere in the world, often at very short notice.

I don't know whether this is strictly accurate, but it is as much as I can remember from the pamphlet I was given at the recruiting centre. The major scribbles something down, then asks me whether I know where I'm heading if I'm selected for enlistment.

'I'll be going to the Infantry Training Centre in Catterick for twenty-four weeks of drill, fieldcraft, weapons training, fitness, individual and team skills instruction, endurance training, live firing and battle camp, sir.'

The major looks up.

'Very good,' he says. 'Out of the fifty potential recruits that came here, twenty have passed – and you're one of them. Well done.'

*

There are still one or two formalities to go through. I return to the Wembley recruiting centre and swear an oath of allegiance to the Queen, then a date is set for my training. I'm to report to the ITC at Catterick, North Yorkshire, at the end of August – four weeks from now.

Forty per cent of recruits fall by the wayside between signing on and passing out. After a couple of months, I'll know whether I can hack it. Only then will I tell my family back home.

CHAPTER 21

Two weeks after we kick off our training, Al-Qaeda terrorists fly airliners into the World Trade Center and the Pentagon. Our instructors remind us daily that the world is now a very different place, that what we learn here won't just be the difference between pass and fail – it may also be the difference between life and death when we go to war with these people.

*

On the day we graduate as soldiers, we put on a demonstration in front of family and friends. Of the sixty-four recruits that turned up in late August, only twenty-three have passed.

We spend the next week preparing for our move. The 1st Battalion PWRR has just been assigned its armoured infantry role in Kosovo.

I've been assigned to 7 Platoon, C Company. Each company is divided into three thirty-man platoons – 7, 8 and 9 Platoons in the case of C Company – each with four

Warriors: Armoured Infantry Fighting Vehicles (AIFV), each with a 30mm cannon.

Personnel are either vehicle crews or dismounts, the infantrymen who will engage the enemy on the ground once they have been delivered to the heart of the action by the Warrior. I'm a dismount, but I can't wait to pass the tests and get behind the wheel of a Warrior.

Our training carries on after we graduate. Proficiency level CP1 means you can fire a rifle and eat out of a mess tin. CP2 means being able to function tactically at platoon level, CP3 at company level and CP4 within a battle group. The aim is to get us up to CP5: the highest you can achieve. We're being trained for war as part of an armoured brigade.

In my spare time I've been learning all I can about the Warrior. The Warrior is an armed and armoured taxi that weighs more than twenty-five tonnes. Technically the Warrior is supposed to be capable of ferrying seven fully equipped soldiers around the battlefield, but normally it's no more than three or four. There really isn't a lot of room in the back: a bench seat to the right and left of the door, and the wall space behind them stuffed so full of equipment that it looks like a quartermaster's store. The commander and gunner sit in an electrically operated turret, behind a Rarden cannon, which can fire 30mm high-explosive and armour-piercing rounds for over a mile. Mounted next to the Rarden is a Hughes 7.62mm chain gun, a belt-fed weapon capable of high firepower and great accuracy. But it can be temperamental, the electric feed system that draws the ammunition from where it's stored beneath the gun sometimes jams.

*

Our mission is to support the Kosovo Police Service, the KPS, while they rebuild what was destroyed in the 1999 war. We're based in a barracks in Pristina, the capital, and most of our duties as dismounts are extremely dull. For the first three months we spend a lot of our time guarding a Serb church that the Muslims keep threatening to burn down.

Occasionally we go out on patrol in our Snatch Land Rovers. We're told that there isn't as much battle damage in Pristina as there is elsewhere, but when I do see a house with its roof blown off, or scorch marks around blown-out windows, I wonder how it came to this. Most of the damage was done by the Serb militia, who shelled the town when they were forced to retreat from it. Pristina used to have a Serb population of forty thousand out of a total of half a million, and almost all of them have fled. A few hang on, like the people who attend the church we guard. I see children with no legs, hobbling on crutches, and old women with blankets over their shoulders. The men stare at us as they file in through the doors. At first I think they look on us as saviours. Later, when my patrol route takes me past the main post office – a tall, abandoned block, its windows blown out by NATO bombs – I realize that they see us as no different from the people we're protecting them against.

I can't get my head around it. Everybody hates everybody. The place is a mess.

*

I get on the course for the Warrior, and after a week of theory and three weeks of maintenance instruction I'm allowed to take my first driving lesson. The aluminium armour is lightweight compared with the steel hull of a main battle tank, but it's designed to provide protection against 14.5mm armour-piercing rounds, 155mm air-burst shell fragments and nine-kilogram anti-tank mines. The driver's position is at the front of the vehicle, to the left of the power pack as you look down from the turret. Standard operating procedure is to drive with the hatch open, your head partly exposed – heads-up. The front of the vehicle slopes downwards at thirty degrees, so the driver has a good field of view. When you have to close the hatch under high threat or combat conditions, things get complicated. You're protected from small-arms fire but can only see out through a periscope – known as a day sight – no bigger than a letterbox. For night missions, or when the vehicle is enveloped in battle smoke, the day sight can be switched to a passive night-vision system. The noise inside a Warrior on the move is so bad that you can't even make yourself heard by shouting, so you communicate via an internal radio network.

The driver is separated from the rest of the crew by a two-metre-long tunnel. I like the feeling of independence this gives, but some drivers hate the isolation. The tunnel is the driver's only means of escape if the vehicle turns over or the hatch jams shut in an emergency. It leads to a cage that surrounds the base of the turret mechanism.

As well as holding ammunition and a maintenance kit, the cage is designed to prevent the gunner and commander from losing their hands and feet as the turret traverses. However, as it doesn't provide all-round protection, it isn't fail-safe. 'Tankies' are full of stories of people who have lost fingers, hands and even feet in the turret mechanisms of tanks and armoured personnel carriers.

If there is an emergency and I need to use the tunnel, I must first wriggle past the cage, into the base of the turret, and from there make my way into the dismounts' section. You can activate the electrically powered door from the back of the vehicle by hitting a button or, if the power is down, crank it open with a T-shaped handle known as a 'ram' that sits under one of the seats. A panel to the left of the U-shaped steering wheel tells me that the vehicle is in neutral. The transmission system, which is fully automatic, has four forward speeds and one reverse. I clasp the lever that releases the footbrake with my right hand, find the spring-loaded toggle on the side and push it with my thumb. It disengages with a thud. I push the starter button on the control panel above it. Beyond the bulkhead against my right shoulder I feel a surge and then the steady pulse of the power pack as the Warrior roars into life.

A ground instructor stands a few feet away, his eyes locked on mine. His arms are held out in front of him, fists together, knuckles forward. He makes a jab to his right and I turn the steering wheel hard over in a full lock. I then touch the accelerator and the Warrior lurches to the left. If I keep pressing the pedal the vehicle will spin around a full 360 degrees.

I smile. As soon as there are no instructors around I'll give it a go. I follow the instructor's directions, revving more gently, building up the power, and the Warrior glides to the left, as if on a cushion of air. I've carried out my first 'neutral turn'. My second attempt is even better.

'Nice one, Beharry,' says the instructor. 'Shall we head for the open road?'

CHAPTER 22

Two weeks later I pass my Warrior test, despite racking up a couple of 'minor infringements' – one for speeding, the other for overtaking. It's the best thing that has happened to me in a long time.

The day before we fly out of Pristina back to the UK, I dream I'm six again, playing in the roots of my gran's wishing tree. 'Look, Gran,' I shout as I spin the bucket lid in my hands. 'Look at me! Look at me! I'm a driver!'

Soon after we touch down at RAF Brize Norton I feel my mobile vibrate. There's a message from Irene, asking me to call her as soon as I get the chance.

'Auntie I,' I say, 'it's me.'

Her voice is faint and there's a lot of distortion on the line, but I know something is wrong. 'Oh, Johnson,' she says. I hear the catch in her voice. 'I'm afraid I have some terrible news.'

'It's me gran, isn't it?' I say.

She doesn't answer, but her silence and the emptiness I feel inside tell me I'm right.

*

I would have preferred a small service, but my gran knew a lot of people and funerals on the island follow a tradition. At the funeral, my cousins and me pick up the coffin, carry it inside and set it down in front of the altar. I manage to hold myself together until the upright piano strikes up the first few bars of 'Blessed Assurance'. I lower my head; I don't want anyone to see me cry.

When the service is over, we follow the horse-drawn hearse up the hill. When it can go no further, we carry the coffin the rest of the way. Everybody crowds around as the priest starts to read the final prayers. The moment he puts down his book, my father, Tan Jane, Abigail and my other aunts and uncles kneel down and place flowers inside the tomb. I have none to give, so I take off my regimental tie and drape it over the coffin.

Two of my cousins pick up the granite slab and set it against the opening. They jiggle it a little and look at each other. Then I hear one of them say, 'It doesn't fit.'

I can't believe it. When it's set against the edge of the tomb it overlaps by two inches.

Somebody calls for a hammer and a chisel, but I take a step forward and push my cousins out of the way.

'All my gran wanted,' I say, unable to hold back my anger, 'all she asked, was to be buried next to her husband. Was that such a difficult thing?'

Nobody answers. I couldn't care less what people think. Isabella Bolah was my grandmother. She was my rescue camp. She loved me and I loved her.

The service fizzles to a halt and the crowd shuffles away. In a couple of minutes, the only people who are left are me, Kellon and my brother Jeffrey. While everybody else is at the wake, the three of us carry a load of bricks and cement up the hill. They offer to help me with the brickwork, but if it's all the same, I tell them, I'd like to do it on my own.

It takes me two hours to get the job done, but I'm not in a hurry. I don't want to join the wake, and this way I get to say goodbye on my own.

A moment before I set the final brick in place I speak the words I've been meaning to say all day.

'Gran,' I tell her, 'I get me wish. Me dream come true.' I listen to the wind. I listen to the leaves. I watch the birds and the insects for some sign that she has heard me. 'I did it, Gran. I get to be a driver.'

CHAPTER 23

Al Amarah, Iraq, 2004

The gate is set into a long, high wall and flanked by a pair of reinforced watchtowers covered with camouflage netting. As we present our papers, the sentry glances over his shoulder at the dark area of scrubland opposite the camp. He waves us through and we park up close to the headquarters building. I climb out of the low-loader. Two hundred metres off, a Chinook helicopter beats its way into the night sky from a floodlit landing pad. I shield my eyes, nose and mouth from the sandstorm it whips up as it roars over us and disappears into the night. I can make out a vehicle park to the left of the headquarters building, crammed with Warriors and Land Rovers. As we retrieve our kitbags from the back of the vehicles, the regimental quartermaster sergeant shows up. Dave Ashton was with the advance party that has been here for the past week preparing for our arrival. He motions for us to follow him.

'Man,' Sammy says, 'I had no idea Abu Naji was goin' to be this big.'

We've had the briefs and been told what to expect, but this is something else. Vehicles come and go the whole time. Another helicopter comes in to land. There's dust everywhere even though it's the middle of the night. Abu Naji used to be an Iraqi Army corps headquarters. They never got round to finishing the place. It's littered with half-finished bunkers and buildings, and dotted with the stumps of dead palm trees. This is now the main military base for 1 PWRR battle group, led by Colonel Maer.

The BG is made up of a squadron of Challenger 2 tanks from the Queen's Royal Lancers, a company of Royal Welch Fusiliers and our own C Company and HQ Company. Y Company, 1 PWRR's recce and mortar unit, is five-and-a-half klicks up the road in a place called Al Amarah. Their job is to protect the Coalition Provision Authority (CPA), based in CIMIC House, a secure compound in the centre of the town. Our job is to police Maysan province, of which Al Amarah is the capital, for the next six months and assist the ICDC maintain law and order.

Everyone has told us that our Kosovo tour will serve as the model: a combination of foot patrols, Land Rover patrols and vehicle checkpoints, or VCPs. The area is heavily populated with rival tribes, many of which have been enemies for centuries. Up until now the Light Infantry have mostly got caught up in their crossfire. Since there seems to be at least one AK47 assault rifle for every household around here, these incidents could get ugly – but not as ugly as the stuff the Americans have had to put up with further north.

Sergeant Major Ashton points out some of the facilities: a pair of shipping containers, known as Caramecs, filled with tables and computer terminals – our local internet café; more Caramecs, converted into shower blocks; the NAAFI, the laundry and, way in the distance, the cookhouse.

Finally we reach a row of tents. We chuck our bags on to our beds. This is where I, Sammy, Campbell, Rushy, Big Erv and the rest of 8 Platoon will be sleeping for our first couple of nights. We can only move into our Caramecs when the LI move out in another couple of days.

Sergeant Chris Adkins – now part of the intelligence section in the Ops Room – sticks his head into our tent.

'At 0700 hours tomorrow you're to report to the Warrior park. The company commander is going to brief you.'

I'm getting undressed in the darkness when I hear what sounds like a vehicle backfiring in the distance. Moments later there is a high-pitched whistle followed by a bang. From the back of the tent, Charlie Malloy, another 8 Platoon driver, says, 'I think that was a mortar going off.'

If it was, I'm too tired to care. I check that my helmet and body armour are within reach under the bed, then roll over and fall asleep.

*

In the cookhouse the next morning I run into Broomstick and Mr Deane.

'How're you doing, Bee?' the boss asks, as we line up for breakfast.

'Good, sir.' I feel myself smiling. 'Now we can do the job we trained for.'

'Did you hear that mortar go off last night?'

'I heard somet'ing. Was it close?'

'Close enough,' he replies. He looks thoughtful. Then he says: 'There's this place called Majar al-Kabir – Mak for short. It's where those RMPs got killed last year. You remember?'

It made all the papers. Two of the RMPs were killed on the spot. The other four surrendered to the mob and were shot with their own weapons.

'Me and the commander went there two days ago as part of a patrol,' Mr Deane continues. 'They thought it'd be a good idea to get some of us over to Mak as part of the hand-over process. So we took three Snatches, and on the way in, just outside the town, we got stoned by a bunch of kids. Then someone fired an RPG at us. We're driving out of the town and I'm standing up, trying to get a bearing on the launch point, when there's another almighty whoosh and a second RPG passes right over my head. We skedaddle out of there as fast as we can after that, I tell you.' He takes another bite of his roll. 'I'm rather hoping that's going to be our little excitement for the tour.'

*

As we line up in front of the Warriors, Major Coote is already waiting. He's a bit like the boss: not too tall, but built like a rugby player and full of energy. He starts by welcoming us to Abu Naji.

'Two weeks ago a number of things happened that may have contributed to a destabilization of the situation here in Maysan province,' he says. 'It's too early to be certain – we're still monitoring the situation, but here is what we know. The Americans decided to shut down a newspaper belonging to Muqtadar Al-Sadr; it was reporting anti-Coalition Force propaganda as fact and winding everybody up. They also arrested one of Al-Sadr's sidekicks – a joker called Yacubi. As some of you are already aware,' – the major looks at Mr Deane as he says this – 'these two incidents have kicked off a backlash here in Al Amarah and the surrounding area, where Al-Sadr is a bit of a folk hero. As the advance party of the 1 PWRR BG, we have already experienced some of that backlash at first hand.'

Major Coote was also in the Snatch convoy that was ambushed in Mak. The backlash he is talking about didn't stop there. Three thousand people rioted in Al Amarah on 3 April, a few days before the 1 PWRR advance party set foot in Abu Naji.

I think about last night's mortar attack.

'We're still trying to assess what this all means,' the OC says. 'We know that there are at least three hundred members of the Mahdi Army within Al Amarah. The Mahdi Army is loyal to Muqtadar Al-Sadr, and Al-Sadr is an angry man right now. The next few days are going to be critical. With any luck the excitement will all die down and we can get into our routine – the job we came here to do.

'We know very little about how the Mahdi Army is organized, but we do know that they are well armed and we have to assume they are capable of causing us trouble if they want to. Over the next few days, as the Light Infantry hand over the ropes, we'll need to keep our eyes peeled and our ears open.'

I still can't get my head around this place. I don't understand why we've allowed the Iraqis to keep their weapons, and I don't understand why the Mahdi Army is left free to roam the streets.

'The whole world is a mess,' Sammy says. 'Why should Iraq be any different?'

CHAPTER 24

'I tell you, Beharry, this really is a pile of old junk. I can't even get the hatch to shut properly,' Jimmy Bryant says through my headset.

It's been more than two years since I last saw Jimmy. Our reunion isn't getting off to a good start. We're less than a minute out of the gates of the camp and already he's dissing Whisky Two Zero.

We're deployed as a mixed-crew vehicle – part Light Infantry, part PWRR – on my first patrol into Al Amarah.

'She shuts fine,' I tell him. 'You just need to put some muscle into it.'

'I am,' he says. 'I'm telling you, mate, the damn thing's stuck.'

The platoon leader, sitting in our turret in place of Mr Deane, tells us both to shut up. All the main routes into and out of Al Amarah have been colour-coded for ease of recognition, but they still don't make a lot of sense to me. Red Route – Route 6 from Basrah – lies ahead. It's a long, straight stretch of highway that leads from Abu Naji camp into the centre of the town, running along the west bank of a tributary of the Tigris. Blue Route runs north–south along the opposite bank. From the map it looks like Al Amarah's two rivers link up at its northern edge to form a 'T'. Purple Route branches off Red Route and loops back towards the town centre from the west, cutting Red Route in half by a tall water tower at the northwest corner of a large housing quarter, at a junction known as Red Eleven. When you see the water tower you know you're in the centre of the city.

Jimmy tells me the OMS is on the opposite side of the river, next to a junction at a road bridge called Yellow Three.

'What's the OMS?' I ask.

'The Office of the Martyr Sadr – the local HQ of the Mahdi Army.'

Major Coote has been talking about the Mahdi Army, but I still don't really get what they do or why they are here.

'What's so special about it?' I ask.

'The OMS? It's supposed to be stuffed with weapons – RPGs, 120mm mortars, 107mm rockets – or that's what we're told. Enough hardware to start a war.'

'If there's weapons in there, why don't we do somet'ing about it?' I ask.

'For the same reason they let anybody carry an AK47. Nobody wants to stir up trouble,' he says. 'Anyhow, as of tomorrow, it's not my problem. It's yours.'

Most of the town's other major landmarks – the police HQ, the telecoms building, the TV station, the bus station and CIMIC House, the CPA's administrative centre – are bordered by Red and Blue Routes north of Red Eleven and Blue Nine. It's forty degrees plus now. I've never felt anything like it, even at home. As we continue along Red Route, moving north, I feel like I've got my face in an oven. To my left, Sparrowhawk, the Coalition airbase to the north-west of Abu Naji, shimmers in the heat. A little further on, just after Purple Route splits off from Red Route, we pass what used to be a prison, codenamed Broadmoor.

The air is thick with the smell of human waste and chemicals that burn the back of my throat. The chemical smell comes from the brick factories on the outer limits of the town; the human waste smell from the slow-moving river alongside us. There's no sewage system to speak of in Al Amarah. It all empties into the waterways and only washes down into the Tigris when the rain comes. We're now into the hot season and it will stay like this well into October. We're just going to have to get used to the stink.

*

'OK, this is it, the moment we've been waiting for,' Mr Deane says, as we gather around our vehicles under the glare of lights in the tank park. 'Operation Pimlico, our chance to take the initiative for a change.'

The plan is for A Company Royal Welch Fusiliers to

go into the housing district just to the north of us, snatch around a dozen people who've been identified as the leaders of the unrest movement and bring them back to Abu Naji for questioning. At long last we're doing something. The housing district, on the southern edge of Al Amarah, is also the place where most of the rocket and mortar attacks have been coming from. The job of 8 Platoon is to conduct a route clearance for the RWF all the way to the outskirts of the town, then wait at Broadmoor, just to the south. From there we'll be ready to give assistance to the RWF if they need it.

Broadmoor is a strange place. It's a prison that never got finished. There's no light or water in the buildings, and rubble all over the place. Despite the heat, most of us prefer to stay in the vehicles rather than hang around the half-finished cell blocks.

'So how come the army has to go in and arrest these people?' Sammy asks. 'I thought the idea was for the local police to take charge.'

'Can't trust 'em, that's the problem,' Mr Deane says. 'More often than not they're the guys who are shooting at us.'

From the traffic over the net it seems that the insurgency leaders are being rounded up and arms and explosives caches found without a shot being fired – until shortly before 0530, when we hear one of the arrest teams report a contact. A couple of minutes later there is another contact, and then another. As the call signs report them, we hear gunshots over the radio, then the crack-crack-crack of small-arms fire not too far away. We get the order to go and help the RWF extract back to Abu Naji; we're directed by Zero to a street corner on Red Route where the dismounts are waiting to be picked up.

The first time we go down the road we see nothing. Mr Deane orders us to turn around and head back, while he checks with Zero on the radio. Then suddenly I spot a group of dismounts moving up an alleyway towards us. Battened down in the Warrior, we don't hear the shots, but I can see them returning fire in the direction they've just come from.

I stamp on the brakes and reverse up to the corner. We open the door and several of the dismounts pile into the back. I hear Sammy traversing the turret, looking for targets, but whoever's doing the shooting remains well hidden, and when we've picked up as many men as we can carry we close the door and move off.

Whisky Two Two and Whisky Two Three take those we can't fit in. The rest get picked up by Saxons and Snatches at rendezvous points where the threat isn't quite as intense.

Back in camp, Broomstick tells me that fourteen suspected insurgent leaders are now under lock and key. After a debrief here they will be sent to Shaiba for interrogation.

Sammy and I are waiting by our vehicle a couple of hours later, when Mr Deane appears.

'There've been some developments,' he says. 'And it doesn't look healthy.'

'I thought Pimlico had been a success,' Sammy says.

'It was a success,' Mr Deane replies. 'So damn successful, in fact, that we've managed to stir up a complete hornet's nest in the process. The Mahdi Army have secured all routes into and out of the city. They've taken some Iraqi policemen hostage and are demanding we release their men in return for their lives.'

CHAPTER 25

Shortly after lunch, 7 and 9 Platoons, led by Major Coote, leave camp. We hear over the net that the two Y Company foot patrols, call signs Three Zero Alpha and Three Zero Bravo, have deployed from the Civil–Military Communications building – CIMIC – and are fanning out to the east and west of the Majidiya Bridge to secure the main route into the compound. By turning right out of camp instead of left on to Red Route, Major Coote is hoping to keep the element of surprise on his side for as long as possible. The problem with Red Route is that it's long and straight and the insurgents can see us coming for miles. A mobile phone call tips off anybody with an AK or an RPG that we're on our way. The re-supply convoy will cross the river and hook up with Blue Route several kilometres to the south of camp and go into the town from there, hitting CIMIC from the west.

Hopefully, Mr Deane says, the Mahdi Army won't have any time to prepare a reception committee. He disappears off in the direction of the Ops Room. The four Warriors of 8 Platoon are lined up facing the gate, engines off but ready to go.

Out of the corner of my eye, I catch movement beyond the door. Others seem to sense it too.

'Oi, oi,' Woody says. 'Something's happening. I just saw the runner.'

Woody gets to his feet. Others get to theirs. The runner is used by the Ops Room to tip off the QRF platoon as soon as something starts to go down.

'Looks like party time,' Woody says. 'Let's go.'

I pick up my helmet and body armour and join the rush for the door. By the time we get outside, the platoon is swarming around the vehicles. I see Mr Deane lowering himself into the commander's hatch of Whisky Two Zero. Engines start. Diesel fumes belch into the air. I pull on my body armour, jump up on to the hull of Whisky Two Zero and slide into my seat.

A couple of seconds later, I have my helmet on and my radio plugged in.

'Boss, Sammy, can you hear me?'

'Roger,' Mr Deane says.

'Loud and clear,' Sammy says.

I check that my SA80 is where I left it, in the foot well next to my knee. I press the starter button. The CV8 diesel roars into life.

'What's happening, Boss?' I ask.

'We're deploying to Blue One. One of the Saxons has broken down, the two Y Company platoons have run into trouble and the OC's taking 7 and 9 Platoons into the town to assist. We'll wait at Blue One and monitor the situation from there.' He checks in with Broomstick, Lewy, Big Joe and the Millennium Falconer. 'OK, Bee,' he says, when all five vehicles are ready, 'Let's roll.'

Soon after we turn out of the gate on to Red Route, we hear a corporal from the Y Company multiple on the east bank, call sign Three Zero Alpha, report that he's holed up in a house between Green Four and Green Nine, surrounded by enemy, with RPG and small-arms fire inbound. His boss, CSM Norman, is watching the battle from the roof of CIMIC House. The corporal can't see them, but he's got more enemy moving towards his position – at least thirty insurgents armed with AKs, heavy machine-guns and RPGs. The situation sounds increasingly desperate. Then we hear a 'zap number' over the net. Somebody is down – shot in the chest at Blue Eleven and in urgent need of a casevac. We hear Whisky Zero Alpha, the OC, transmit that he's moving up to assist. The OC is going to lead 7 and 9 Platoons into the city, come to the aid of the cut-off and pinned-down call signs, dispatch at least one Warrior to bring the casualty back and then drop off the supplies at CIMIC. Two Warriors, meanwhile, are to remain at Blue One to protect the broken-down Saxon.

A couple of minutes later we spot the Saxon and the Warriors and pull on to the side of the road next to them.

Comms on the 'all-inform net', the radio network that is supposed to enable all elements of the battle group to listen and talk to one another, are often patchy; today there are plenty of cut-outs, making it hard to piece together what's happening. We track the OC's Warrior convoy as it moves north into a housing estate close to the river, where Whisky One Zero reports a direct hit by an RPG. The shell penetrates the hull and leads to a loss of power, but Second Lieutenant Styler tells Zero that they are able to continue on task.

The net fills with Warrior commanders reporting that they are engaging enemy positions with their chain guns. Second Lieutenant Plenge reports that Whisky Three Zero has identified the location of the wounded dismount. From his zap number Woody realizes it's a mate of his – Lance Corporal Barry Bliss. Moments later Plenge says they've got Bliss in the back of Whisky Three Zero and are administering first aid, but that his chest wound is serious and he's going downhill fast.

We listen as Plenge sets up a helicopter landing site just down the road from us so they can casevac Bliss to Shaiba. Mr Deane tells Zero we're moving closer to the action.

'Whisky Two Zero. Blue Five, figures five,' he says, indicating five minutes.

As the reserve force it's our job to be as close to the contact area as is reasonably safe, ready to move in the moment we're needed. Blue Five is right on the edge of the town.

We've been at Blue Five no more than a couple of minutes when we hear that the Warriors under the OC's charge have managed to pick up some dismounts and are now offloading them – under fire – along with the food, ammo and water, at CIMIC. The OC says he's heading back into the contact area to extract the other call signs that are still pinned down.

Mr Deane tells Zero that we're moving up into the southern suburbs.

'Whisky Two Zero. Blue Six, figures two …'

I slip the vehicle into drive and head for the houses I can see at the edge of the heat haze.

Water bubbles up from a broken main in the middle of the road. We pass a cart by the side of the road loaded with water melons. The guy who's selling them waves at me as we drive by. We're on the outskirts of the city, just past Blue Six, and he doesn't seem to have a care in the world. I take my eye off the road for a fraction of a second and don't see the woman with the bucket on her head until she's almost under our tracks.

I brake hard and hear Sammy and Woody swear. The woman just carries on walking; I don't think she realizes I'm here, let alone how close I came to killing her. I watch her slip into an alleyway and disappear.

The boss is talking to Zero about trying to follow the OC to Blue Fourteen, but there is nothing wide enough for a Warrior where we are, so we press on to Blue Seven. We can turn right there, but the boss is trying to avoid it as Blue Route north of Blue Seven is a huge boulevard that runs up through the centre of the city, where the Mahdi Army is thickest on the ground.

When the boss isn't talking to the Ops Room, he's giving Woody a running description of the scenery that surrounds us. Every so often he feeds Woody coordinates from his handheld GPS.

I know that Woody is listening hard and following these on his map; he needs to know exactly what to expect in case he, Erv and Clifton suddenly have to jump out of the back.

'We're three hundred metres short of Blue Seven … two-fifty …' Mr Deane says. 'There's flat-roofed houses on the left, more on the right, some single-, some two-storey, you know the kind, same old same old …' He pauses, then says, 'According to the map, there's a road on the right any moment that looks like it could take us up to Blue Fourteen. I'm going to pop my head out and see if I can get eyes-on.'

I hear him open the hatch. A motorcycle overtakes us and makes a right down the next street. It catches my attention, because the guy who's riding pillion has an AK slung across his back. As we approach the turning I see that the bike has turned right round and is now facing us on Blue Route.

The passenger has got off and is hanging with five other guys by a lamp-post on the corner. They are dressed in jeans and T-shirts and three of them are holding AKs. They all stare at us as we rumble past.

'Boss, six guys on our right, some of them with AKs ...'

'Got 'em,' Mr Deane says.

'Don't like the look of 'em much.'

'Isn't that the route up to Blue Fourteen?' I ask.

'Yeah,' he says. 'One of them. Best we keep going.'

He transmits our LOCSTAT to Zero. 'Whisky Two Zero at Red Seven, figures one.'

I see the junction up ahead. In less than a minute the road will veer sharply to the right. Checking my mirror, I see the four other Warriors in the convoy strung out along the street to our rear. Whisky Two Two, Broomstick's wagon, is fifty metres back. The rest are spaced out evenly behind him. Broomstick's turret is traversing from right to left, gun raised at an angle towards the rooftops. Apart from Mr Deane and me, everybody else, as far as I can tell, is battened down.

When I look at the junction again, a voice inside my head is telling me that something is wrong. I ease off the power and we start to slow.

'Bee, what is it?' Mr Deane asks. 'Why are you slowing?'

'Somet'ing ain't right, Boss.'

I look in the mirror and catch another glimpse of the view to our rear. The road behind us is as clear of people as the junction in front, and yet a minute ago – less, maybe – it was busy, busy, busy ...

'There's no people, Boss. Look. Front and back.

Everybody's gone.'

There's a pause, then Mr Deane says, 'Yeah, see what you mean. Better bring her to a stop. I'll check with Zero.'

After they have held a brief discussion about other route options for cutting up to Blue Fourteen, Mr Deane decides to press on. We move forward again. I spot another street on the right. It looks wide enough to take us. Dust kicked up from the platoon's tracks makes it difficult to see, but I realize there's something across it. As the dust clears I see a low barrier made out of rubble, oil drums and an old lamp-post.

'Boss, what now?'

It's our last chance to turn right before the big junction at Blue Seven.

'Can't drive over it,' Mr Deane says. 'There could be an IED in there.' He pauses. 'Looks like we've got no choice now but to move on up Blue Route. Got that, Bee?'

'Got it.'

I slow down as I approach the junction and the Warriors behind me start to bunch. The street we're in is narrow. Houses rise up on either side of us. I snatch quick, nervous glances, left and right, at their flat roofs. I see nothing, no one. The street remains absolutely deserted.

'Hang a right,' Mr Deane says.

Ahead is a typical Saddam boulevard – two lanes either side of a central reservation, with lamp-posts like palm trees, evenly spaced. Five-storey tower blocks rise up on both sides of the road between crumbling, one- and two-storey brick houses. Every thirty metres or so alleyways disappear between the buildings.

I start to make the turn. The four lanes of the boulevard disappear into the distance. The heat from the road twists the lamp-posts out of shape. There isn't a single car on the road.

As I straighten up I see why. Fifty metres in front of us is another makeshift barrier.

'Boss …?'

'I know,' Mr Deane says.

Maybe he's thinking the same thing as me. The first place we want to turn right is blocked by guys on motorcycles. The second has got a barrier across it. We're bunched up on an approach road to a major junction, and now this …

'Damn!' I hear Sammy say.

'What?' the Boss says.

'Left-hand side. There's a kid across the street. Eleven, maybe twelve years old. He's holding what looks like an RPG!'

I'm turning to look when there is a massive explosion and the vehicle shakes like it's been hit by a tidal wave.

'Boss … what was that?' There isn't even a crackle of static in my headphones. 'Boss, what happened?'

Still nothing. Whatever hit us must have messed up our comms. I twist and crane my neck, but the turret blocks my view of anything on top of or behind the vehicle, the boss and Sammy included.

Smelling burning, I glance back down the driver's tunnel. Then I hear someone scream.

CHAPTER 26

I've seen this moment many times in my dreams. My thoughts slow and for a split second I see the mess we have stumbled into as if I'm above the street, looking down. I can't reverse up. Looking for exits ahead, anything that offers protection, I see only the endless boulevard, shimmering in the last of the day's heat. I know that Whisky Two Zero stands out like a doubledecker bus in the glare of the street lights. I hit the accelerator, but the power kicks in a fraction too late. The Warrior lurches and a second detonation punches its back end a metre and a half across the road.

The power pack coughs and for a moment I think Whisky Two Zero is going to die on me. But miraculously the revs pick up again. I point her nose towards the open highway and see the barrier – a line of hastily erected breeze blocks – too late to avoid it. An instant before we crash there is another explosion, even bigger than the last. A pressure wave filled with noise and heat tears past me and out of the hatch.

With little forward speed, Whisky Two Zero grinds against the concrete wall. Deafened by the last explosion,

I don't hear the tracks spinning uselessly on the road surface, but I can feel them. I slip the Warrior into reverse and take her back a few metres. Then I edge forward again, this time targeting the right side of the block.

We hit it hard and my head almost strikes the rim of the hatch. I increase the revs, knowing that the engine, always Whisky Two Zero's weak point, is losing power.

As I brace myself for another explosion I feel movement from the barrier. Whisky Two Zero begins to force her way through. I shout, urging her on as the gap widens until, with a final push, we manage to squeeze through. But the men who erected the barrier know what they're doing. They know our routine. They know we're coming. It's as if they've predicted our every move.

Bang in front of me is a small mound of stones with an aerial sticking out of the top: an IED. The mine is big enough to seriously vex a Challenger tank. What will it do to us?

Again, time slows. All I can think of is the battery of RPGs to my rear. I can't go back. I hear the screaming again. It comes from the back of the vehicle. I know all too well what an RPG does to the inside of a tank. First, the fuse activates the shaped charge penetrator of the high-explosive warhead. In a nanosecond the energy of the explosive focuses on a band of copper wrapped around the charge. The explosion builds from the back of the charge, melting the copper and propelling it forward in a pencil-thin jet capable of cutting a hole through ten centimetres of armour – more than enough to penetrate the hull of a Warrior – and bringing a melon-sized chunk of metal with it. If you're in the path of the jet she'll bore straight through you.

I decide to take my chances with the mine, hoping the power pack alongside me will take the full force of the blast, shielding the men behind me. I pull the hatch closed and the front of the Warrior passes over the antenna.

The Warrior fills with the stench of burning. There's shouting and screaming from the back and the driver's compartment fills with smoke. It catches in the back of my throat. I radio the boss several times, requesting status on the vehicle, but I hear nothing. My headphones are dead. Then I hear someone.

'Boss, Boss, you all right?'

The voice reaches me through the driver's tunnel. There's something strange, almost dreamlike about it. It sounds like it's a long way away.

'Boss, Boss … Talk to me!'

Outside, I know there are more RPGs waiting for us. I can't go back, because the other four Warriors are directly behind me. All I can do is press on. I have little or no space to manoeuvre; I ease Whisky Two Zero to the right. I want to make sure that when the IED goes off, the power pack will shield us from the worst of the blast.

I gun the engine and close my eyes. When I open my eyes

again we're ten metres beyond the barrier and there's been no explosion. The smoke filling the driver's compartment makes it difficult for me to breathe. I throw open the hatch again. Bullets hit the front of the vehicle like hailstones and I look up and see gunmen shooting at us from the rooftops.

Then I hear answering fire from the turret – not the *ratatatatat* of the chain gun, but an SA80 on single shot. Bam, bam, bam. It's Sammy.

'Drive! ' he shouts. 'There's more of 'em lining up with RPGs.'

I tread down on the accelerator, but get very little response from the engine.

'Move, Beharry. Move, move, move! ' Woody yells.

'I'm trying,' I yell, but there's something wrong. The RPG that singed the back of my head went straight into the engine compartment. I don't know how much life Whisky Two Zero has left in her.

Slowly we start to pick up speed. There's a lot of shouting from the back. Erv is yelling he wants to get out so he can take as many of them down as he can. I can hear Woody trying to calm him down. Woody calls out to the boss again.

'Stop calling the boss,' Sammy yells. 'The boss is dead! He's dead! He got hit by the first RPG. He's lying on the floor of the turret. He's a mess, man. A complete mess.'

'What about you, Sammy? You hit?' I yell.

'I got burned. It's burnin' in here.'

'Where's the fire?'

'I dunno. Can't see it. Somewhere on the floor of the turret, I think. Just drive!'

A guy wearing Arab dress runs out into the middle of the street and sprays us with his AK47. I hear the strikes pinging off the armour in front of me.

'Use the chain gun, Sammy, for God's sake!' I shout.

'I can't, man, it's jammed! My SA80 got hit. All I got is the boss's weapon …'

The guy with the AK just stands there. He's fifty metres away and firing from the hip. Something slams into my helmet and my head is thrown back against the hatch. When I open my eyes the guy with the gun is still there.

'Shoot him, Sammy, shoot him!'

The guy keeps firing the AK until the last possible second, then darts into an alleyway as we thunder on down the street.

Black flags hang from the balconies of the houses we pass by. Black flags, a part of me is thinking. What the hell's that all about? Are they for us? Do they know we're going to die here?

A movement in the shadows on the corner of an alleyway catches my eye. A guy steps out. He's wearing a green combat jacket and jeans. He heaves a brown and black tube over his shoulder and fires. Dust flies into the air from the back-blast as the tube kicks upwards. I should have yelled 'RPG!' but I can't. I'm hypnotized by the sight of the shell as it heads straight for us. I've been here before.

At first it seems frozen in space. Then, as I reach up and grab the hatch, the speed picks up and a millisecond before the round hits us I realize it's coming straight for me. I duck and pull the hatch down with a crash and then there is an ear-splitting explosion that tears it out of my grip. A wave of heat and a blast of pressure shoot over my head and on down the tunnel.

There's a scream behind me and I realize that Sammy has been caught by the explosion. I sit up and open my eyes. I stare through the day sight but I can't see a thing. The RPG must have exploded against it, destroying it completely.

The engine coughs again and for the first time I feel the heat from the bulkhead between me and the power pack. I throw open the hatch, breathe in a huge lungful of air and press down on the accelerator. Whisky Two Zero judders.

'Sammy!'

Nothing. I hear the sound of an extinguisher going off. There's more yelling and screaming from the back. And then I remember. The extinguisher isn't meant to be operated when there are people inside the vehicle – it sucks the oxygen out in a heartbeat.

No time to think about that now … The road seems to stretch all the way to the horizon. The street lights appear like matchsticks in the distance. I don't see any gunmen, but I can still hear the rain of bullets on the hull. I know I've got to get us out of the killing zone. I know I've got to get us off this road. But which way do I go? I can't raise the rest of the platoon; our comms are totally broken. All I know is that CIMIC is somewhere at the end of Blue Route and the rest of the company is somewhere near CIMIC. Trouble is, I've never been there before and I don't know the road.

I check the mirror and see the other vehicles. They're following me and firing back with their chain guns at the gunmen on the roofs. They're following me because they think Mr Deane is still in charge of the platoon; they don't realize he's dead.

Dead. The boss. I can't believe it.

I press my foot to the floor and check the speedo, but we can barely raise thirty-five miles per hour. The heat from the engine compartment is adding to the sweltering conditions inside the Warrior. How much longer can we last before the power pack gives up on us, or just blows up?

Don't go there, Johnson, I tell myself. Just concentrate on getting us out of this mess ...

I start to weave, left and right, down the boulevard. With our speed dropping off I know we present an easy target for another strike by an RPG. We've been hit by at least four; we can't take another. A fresh volley of small-arms fire, and this time I see the sparks as the bullets crack and fly off the armour. I can see no end to the killing zone and for the first time I feel real fear. If I mess up now, it's not just going to be the boss, me, Sammy, Erv, Wood and Clifton that will pay the price. Where I go, the platoon follows.

I hold the little cross by my neck and as I pray I hear the words of a song: 'Angels descending bring from above, Echoes of mercy, whispers of love …'

'Gran,' I whisper, 'please help me …'

There's an opening on the left. I know I have to take it. I swing Whisky Two Zero into the turn. The street is narrower than I thought. It bunches in front of me. I start to panic. What if the road runs out? What if we get caught in this rat run?

CHAPTER 27

Sammy starts to scream. The blast from the last RPG must have knocked him out. He's alive, but in terrible pain. From the sound of it, I know he's burning …

'Sammy?' I shout. 'Sammy? Can you hear me?'

He doesn't respond. More shouting from the back. Sammy isn't the only one who's wounded. Someone – it sounds like Erv – is yelling that Clifton has got a huge piece of shrapnel sticking out of his face.

Suddenly another road opens up to the right. It looks wider than the street we're on and I decide to take it.

I fire Whisky Two Zero into the turn and check that the others are still behind; they are. For the moment the shooting has stopped. I gun the engine. It coughs and splutters and I know from the sound she's making that she won't last much longer.

I check that my SA80 is still in the foot well, and am about to yell to Woody that we're probably going to have to get out and fight, when I see another Warrior at the end of the street. It's so unexpected that for a moment I wonder if it's my imagination. I blink, but the Warrior is still there, by a crossroads, angled away from the street we're on. I'm not sure it has seen us.

'Sammy! Woody!' I yell. 'There's a Warrior dead ahead. Hang in there, all right?'

I get no reply. I daren't take my eyes off the Warrior. Without comms I have no way of attracting its attention. Stay there. Please. A few seconds longer ...

We make it. As I pull up alongside, the hatch opens and the commander's head appears. When he turns my way I realize it's Major Coote, the OC. I can see him talking into his mike, but because my comms are shot I can hear nothing. I look at him, tap my helmet, then jab a thumb behind me in the direction of the turret. I draw a finger across my throat. The OC hesitates for no more than a second. I'm telling him Mr Deane is dead and I know how badly this news must hit him. He touches the top of his head – the signal for me to follow him.

I stick to his tail. The road makes a sweeping turn to the left, hugging a bend in the river. Suddenly the ground opens up and there's a walled compound on my right, ringed by barriers of galvanized steel and polypropylene, with a stone-built guard post out front. Beyond the OC's vehicle, in the middle of the open ground, is a Warrior out on its own. Two more are lined up alongside the barrier. Some dismounts are crouched down by the vehicles and firing at targets to my left.

The vehicles' chain guns are shooting in the same direction. More dismounts are chucking boxes over the barrier. It's chaos, but at least we've made it to CIMIC House.

Major Coote pulls up in front of the Warrior in the middle of the clearing. Bullets spatter the hull of his Warrior. Seconds later I hear them do the same to us. I pull up a few metres behind the OC's wagon and look to my left.

Fifty metres away is the edge of another run-down housing development. Washing lines and TV aerials jut out of an endless sea of flat roofs. The perfect vantage point for enemy snipers. The barrier to my right marks the edge of the CIMIC compound. Beyond it I can make out palm trees, a large concrete water tower, and in the distance, right by the river, the roof of CIMIC House itself.

The smell of burning is getting stronger. I look down. The heat from the bulkhead wall is so bad that in places I can see it glowing red.

As I pull myself out of the hatch four or five rounds ricochet off the front of the Warrior. My God, someone is targeting me!

I drop back down into my seat. My hands are shaking. If I sprint through the bullets and throw myself over the barrier, I say to myself, I'll be safe.

Choices. The boss is dead. Whisky Two Zero is my vehicle; she's my pride and joy. Sammy, Woody, Erv and Clifton all need my help.

I pull myself out of the hatch.

A bullet whines through the air above my head. I crouch down beside the turret. There's a burst of machine-gun fire from the flat roofs and an answering volley from a chain gun somewhere close by. I roll on to the turret, hugging the hot metal.

The hatch is still open. I smell burning. *Crack!* A bullet hits the turret a foot from my face. I move closer. When I lean over the hatch I see Mr Deane slumped across the floor, face down, the back of his head covered by his helmet. There is blood on his seat and the shredded remains of his body armour on the ammunition rack. He must have caught the full blast of the first RPG.

I lean inside and tap the back of his helmet. He doesn't move. But something in the corner of the turret does.

Sammy is hunched, clutching his sides, head lowered. An explosion has ripped the clothes from his upper body. His chest is peppered with burns.

'Sammy, man, it's me.'

He turns towards me and there are burns all over his face as well. When he opens his eyes they are blood-red. I'm not sure he can see me. He reaches out for me and I grab him by the wrist. I start to pull him towards me. A bullet hits the hatch. I let go and he falls back.

The boss groans. Jesus Christ, the boss is alive.

I look at Mr Deane and I look at Sammy. Smoke is

pouring into the turret from deep inside the vehicle. The heat is unbelievable. I don't know how long we have before the vehicle blows. All I know is I've got to get the boss out. I reach down, take hold of his shirt and pull. I manage to lift him a little, but he's too heavy and he slips from my grip. Mr Deane is twice my weight. I'm never going to do it.

'Sammy, man, you got to help me lift the boss. I can't lift him on me own.'

Fumbling, Sammy grabs hold of a part of the boss's shirt and pulls. Mr Deane's head comes up a fraction and before Sammy lets go, I grab hold of the boss's helmet. I know I have only one shot at this. I pull with all my might and manage to get the boss into an upright position.

Another bullet cracks off the hatch, but I ignore it. This time I'm not letting go. I place my feet either side of the hatch and pull. Mr Deane starts to make a terrible choking sound, but his head and upper body are through the mouth of the hatch. If I let go now I'll never get him back up.

A volley of bullets cracks and whines off the side of the vehicle. I'm not letting go. With a roar, I pull, and as I do I feel the muscles in my back rip in all kinds of places. I – am – not – letting – go …

Mr Deane's body flops out of the hatch on to the top of the turret. A bullet thuds into the armour a couple of inches from his helmet. I take a deep lungful of air. There's a terrible red welt on the boss's neck where his helmet strap has dug into his skin. But he's breathing, he's alive.

I take hold of one of his arms and drag him on to my shoulders. My back is agony but I'm not letting go. I make my way to the front of the vehicle. I can hear the OC's chain gun providing me with covering fire as I lay Mr Deane's body as gently as I can on the sloping armour. Then I jump down on to the ground, pull the boss more firmly on to my shoulders and carry him as quickly as I can to the back of the OC's vehicle.

The door opens and I hand him over. I don't know who to, and I don't care. Now I have to go and get Sammy.

On my way back to Whisky Two Zero, I see the other four vehicles of the platoon for the first time. They are parked up next to the barrier, their chain guns pouring fire into the housing development. I can see Falconer, the CSM, hurling ammunition boxes over the barrier. The vehicles are too far away for me to be able to get anybody's attention. If I tried to make it over there, I would be cut down by fire from the rooftops. They have their own problems; I have mine. I'm on my own.

Sammy is already halfway out of the commander's hatch when I jump back on to the hull.

'Come on,' I say, grabbing him by the wrist.

There's so much blood on his face I'm still not sure he can see.

'What happened, man?' he asks.

I don't know, I tell him. And now's not the time to be talking about it.

We hear another burst of gunfire from the housing estate and I pull him down below the level of the turret. A volley of shots rakes the front of the vehicle. I hop down on to the ground and drag Sammy after me. Then I turn to the OC's wagon. It's disappeared.

For a moment I'm confused, then just plain angry. Where's it gone? But then I remember: as the command vehicle, its dismount section is stuffed full of radio kit. There's room in the back for just one person – Mr Deane. And the Warrior he parked next to is still there, its rear door open.

Holding Sammy with one arm, I start to make my way to it. Just before I get there I look up and see the OC's vehicle reversing towards us. It screeches to a halt alongside the other vehicle and starts hammering at the flat roofs fifty metres away with its chain gun.

Sammy groans.

'It's OK,' I tell him. 'You're safe now.'

We make it to the shelter of the Warrior. I climb in the back and sit him down on one of the bench seats.

'I can't stay with you, Sammy. I have to go back.'

I turn around and head back towards Whisky Two Zero. Smoke is pouring from the commander's hatch.

I run around to the rear. The door is open a crack. I take hold of it and yank it back.

'Son of a bitch, I'm gonna kill you!'

Hearing this, I jump backwards, scared out of my skin. Big Erv is pointing his SA80 at my chest. There's blood on his face and a wild look in his eyes. He's a split second away from pulling the trigger.

'Erv, it's Beharry!'

Woody appears out of the smoke at the back of the dismount section. Erv lowers his rifle. He's bleeding from a gaping wound just below one of his knees. Woody is a mess too. His face is covered in cuts. His helmet has been blown off and he's missing most of his hair. There's blood on the floor and the walls.

I can see daylight through the left-hand wall, where the molten jet of the RPG scythed through the armour and the turret cage.

'Erv, where's Clifton?'

Big Erv stares at me vacantly. He's slumped back against the wall of the Warrior, cradling his SA80.

'I dunno, he just … went …' I hear something behind me. I swing round, half-expecting to see an Iraqi with an AK. But I'm confronted by a sergeant, one of the guys from Y Company, based in CIMIC House.

'You lot,' he says, 'move, now. This wagon is on fire!'

'We're missing a man, a dismount,' I tell him. 'Clifton. Big guy, got a piece of shrapnel in the face …'

'Oh, him!' the sergeant says. 'I've just seen him. He's

inside the compound. Didn't realize he was one of yours …'

Clifton, at least, is safe. The sergeant pulls Woody and Erv out of the back and the four of us rush over to the vehicle I've left Sammy in. As soon as Erv and Woody are safely in the back, I sprint over to the OC.

Major Coote is hunkered down behind the open hatch. 'Sir, what do I …?'

'Follow me. We're going to drive out of the contact area.'

Ducking bullets, I'm halfway back to Whisky Two Zero when I realize that the OC doesn't know how badly damaged she is. I hear the rev of engines as his Warrior and the one with Sammy, Erv and Woody on board get ready to move out. I climb back on to the hull of Whisky Two Zero and drop into the driver's hatch. It's too late to do anything else. Smoke is pouring out of her engine vents, but the power pack is still running – I can feel the pedals vibrate through the soles of my boots.

The two Warriors ahead of me neutral-turn and start to move off, heading back the way we came. I release the handbrake and pray Whisky Two Zero can still drive. She hops forward, but after less than a hundred metres she starts to judder. The entire bulkhead separating me from the engine compartment is now glowing. The power pack has done all she can. Now she's giving up the ghost.

The OC stops. He knows I'm in trouble. I coax Whisky Two Zero alongside his vehicle and tell him the problem.

'Go back to CIMIC and dump it,' he shouts. 'We'll wait for you here.'

On the way back Whisky Two Zero is hit by another volley of shots from the housing estate. The four other 8 Platoon wagons are still parked up next to the compound. The guys are still heaving ammunition and food boxes over the wall into CIMIC House. If Whisky Two Zero blows, she could take them with her. If she doesn't, she could fall into enemy hands.

I'm wondering where I can dump her that's both safe and secure. I see the barricade that marks CIMIC's outer perimeter. Its concrete blocks will absorb most of the blast if Whisky Two Zero blows.

I drive back into the killing zone and manoeuvre the vehicle so that I get the barrier between me and the other wagons. I switch off the engine, reach over to my right and pull the handle that triggers the fire extinguishers. There's a whooshing noise behind the bulkhead and a cloud of white vapour pours out of the vents.

I grab my SA80, spare ammo clips and belt kit, clamber out of the driver's hatch and haul myself on to the top of the vehicle. I place the rifle and the belt kit on the hull and ease myself into the turret through the commander's hatch.

As I drop to the ground my legs give way and I fall face down into the dirt. Then I hear gunfire again and the spatter of bullets nearby.

I pull myself back on to my feet. I stagger around to the back of Whisky Two Zero and pull my day sack from the rack, then Sammy's and the boss's. Weighed down by three day sacks and two SA80s, I turn and run towards the waiting Warriors.

Sammy and Erv are seated towards the back of the compartment. Woody is sitting by the door. I collapse on the seat opposite him. The door closes. It feels like I've been sealed inside an oven. I try to breathe, but I can't. The vehicle moves and I tip forward, ending up with my head on the floor, alongside Sammy's feet.

'Get his helmet off!' I hear somebody yell.

And then I can't hear or see anything else at all.

CHAPTER 28

I'm lying in the semi-darkness. I hear no vehicles, no helicopters, just the faint sound of the wind shaking the canvas above my bed. A dim light glows on around twenty other beds. I remember people ripping my body armour off me and a medic yelling for water, lots of it. At some point I asked one of the medical staff, a female doctor, about my mates. She told me that Sammy, Mr Deane, Woody and Erv were safe. They'd been stabilized in camp, then transferred to the hospital at Shaiba. She told me that there's nothing wrong with me, either, except heat exhaustion, and that all I need is a lot of rest.

The next morning I get dressed and walk out of the Med Centre. The staff protest; they want to keep me under observation. But they can't keep me in. There's nothing physically wrong with me. They can observe me from a distance.

On the way back to the accommodation block I run into the OC and Falconer. 'Ah, Beharry,' the CSM says, 'we were on our way over to see you.' 'He holds up a helmet. It's my helmet. I look down and see that there's a hole in the top of it and a groove about three inches long. I hear the sound of gunfire in my head; the guy coming out of the shadows, firing an AK from the hip; me shouting at Sammy to use the chain gun, then something slamming into my helmet with such force that my neck snapped back against the hatch …

'I want to tell you that what you did yesterday was outstanding,' he says. 'And Richard Deane is going to be just fine, thanks to you. He's got the headache from hell and they're still picking bits of RPG out of him, but they think he'll be back inside a week. The same goes for Samuels, Wood and Ervin.' Then he smiles as he turns my helmet over.

Something is sticking through the lining.

'I thought you'd be interested to see this. The round is still in there. Your helmet stopped a 7.62. That's a pretty close shave you had there, Beharry. Well done.'

CHAPTER 29

The days pass, rolling into weeks. Mr Deane and the others get patched up. We roll on. Day after day, attacks and counter-attacks.

At one-thirty on the morning of 11 June we're sitting in our vehicles when we get scrambled. A mortar has just been fired at Abu Naji from somewhere within the grid. If we're quick we can get them.

Twenty seconds after we turn on to Red Route, Whisky Two Two tucked in behind us, the lights go out. They know we're coming. There's no moon and we're driving with our lights off and for a moment I can't see a thing.

I take my foot off the accelerator and we start to slow.

'Bee, what are you doing?' Mr Deane says.

He is tucked down inside the turret, plotting our route to the grid reference that Zero has just sent us.

'I can't see nothing, Boss. I think we're coming up to Red Eight, but I'm not sure. I never known it so dark.' '

OK,' Mr Deane says, 'give us a couple of secs and I'll stand up and take a look.'

I hear the clang of the hatch on the turret. I know

Mr Deane is up there, scanning through his night sight. The CWS works better than the night-vision setting on the day sight. I flip my hatch down and take a look too.

Ahead the street sparkles in shades of green and black as my optics struggle to cope with the absence of light. All I see is Red Route disappearing into the distance; open scrub to the right; alleyways leading into the grid between a chequerboard of houses on our left.

'Looks to me like we're around fifty metres short of Red Eight,' Mr Deane says.

I agree.

I throw open the hatch and gently press down on the accelerator. We edge towards the junction. I'm looking for the turning to Purple Four and cursing the fact it's so dark.

There's a flash off to the left. Mr Deane shouts a warning; Sammy yells my name. I see something out of the corner of my eye. The nose of a shell, flipped-out fins, a plume of smoke … less than a Warrior's length away.

There's a flash of light and an unholy crash and something slams into my head. I get a ringing in my ears and a metallic taste in my mouth.

I open my eyes but I can't see. I try to remember where I am, what I'm supposed to be doing, but I can't.

'Bee?' Mr Deane is talking to me. 'Bee, can you hear me? Get us out of here! Go, go, go!'

I slip into reverse and hit the accelerator. We shoot

backwards.

'Whoa!' Mr Deane shouts.

Got to get us out of the kill zone. Got to get us away from here. Go faster. Faster …

A flash of tracer … We're not on a road. We're racing backwards across open ground … What am I doing here? We hit something and stop. Shouting. Gunfire. Darkness.

Something slides out of the darkness and parks in front of us. Another Warrior.

Broomstick and Mr Deane are talking. Mr Deane is hurt. He's got a cut on his head, but he says he's OK. I've got a cut on mine too. I try to reach up and touch it, but my arm won't move.

In front of me, the Warrior starts to move away.

'Follow him, Bee,' Mr Deane says.

'OK,' I tell him. But I can't move my foot either. What's happening to me?

'I got you, mate. You're OK now.'

I look up. Broomstick. Staring down at me. What's he doing here?

He takes hold of one arm. Somebody else grabs the other one. They pull. Lift me out. Next thing I know, I'm in the back of a Warrior.

I open my eyes. Broomstick is still looking down at me. My head is in his lap.

'Stick? That you?'

'Yeah, mate, it's me.'

'What's happening to me?'

'You're going to be all right, Harry. Now hold still, mate, while I put this dressing on you.' Tears are rolling down his face. Tears …

'Stick?'

'Yeah, mate?'

'Am I dying?'

'Nah, mate, you're not dying.'

'It hurts, Stick. It hurts.'

'Hang in there, Harry, we're nearly there, mate, nearly there …'

The door opens. I'm carried into Broadmoor.

People stare at me strangely. It's like they've just seen a ghost. I'm laid out on a stretcher. Straps are placed across my legs and chest. Radios crackle. Somebody's talking about a helicopter flight.

I try to get up, but I can't. A girl with blonde hair comes up to me and plunges a needle in my leg.

'My head hurts,' I tell her. 'I need to get up, see me gran. She can fix me. She can fix me good.'

'You're not going anywhere,' she says.

The radio crackles again. 'IRT Chinook's warming up on the pad at Abu Naji,' a voice says. I feel myself starting to slide. I'm going on a journey. I wish I knew where.

CHAPTER 30

0830 hours, 19 June 2004

I'm lying on a hospital bed with no memory of how I got here. The sheets are clean and cool. The walls are bare, except for a clock above the door. Everything is white – the sheets, the walls, the blinds, the monitoring equipment, even the face of the clock.

*

0630 hours, 21 June 2004

Although I'm sedated, I'm aware of what is going on around me; the pain makes sure of that. Details of the attack have started to filter back: deploying from Broadmoor, slowing down at Red Eight, a flash off to the left, the explosion in front of my face … Then nothing.

*

My head is so swollen I can hardly open my eyes. When I do, I see double. I'm fitted up to drips that are meant to control the pain, but they don't. I feel like someone's mashing up the front of my head with a sledgehammer.

*

I find out later my injuries are amongst the worst anyone has ever seen. The pressure wave from the explosion caused multiple fractures to my skull. My forehead has been crushed. The doctor says: 'Imagine what happens to an eggshell when you hit it hard with a spoon; that's what happened to your skull. There's bone damage in the area of your eye sockets, and your brain itself has suffered a burst right frontal lobe.'

I don't take any of this in. All I know is, I hurt.

*

Two days after I come out of coma, I'm heavily sedated, put into an ambulance and driven to the airport. The priority now, the doctors say, is to get me to the Neuroscience Centre in Birmingham.

I'm airborne on an RAF TriStar. I drift in and out of consciousness until we arrive at RAF Brize Norton. It's a two-hour ride in an ambulance to the University Hospital in Selly Oak, Birmingham.

Over the next three days I'm scanned, X-rayed and visited by consultants. Some of the doctors try to tell me about the operation, but I find it hard to listen. Concentration only makes the pain worse.

I'm in a room by myself. Captain Wright has arranged for the next-door room to be kept for Aunt Irene. She's been joined by Darren and Gavin, who are staying in a nearby hotel. I don't want to see anyone else.

I know the operation is risky. I see the look on everyone's face. But right now my head hurts so bad, I don't care whether I live or die. I just want them to take the pain away.

*

RAF Headley Court is a big red-brick mansion set in eighty-five acres of landscaped gardens and rolling fields near Leatherhead in Surrey. It's the home of the Defence Services Medical Rehabilitation Unit, a treatment centre for people in the armed forces who have sustained serious spine and limb injuries.

I'm given an extensive neurological examination. They find nothing wrong with my attention, my concentration, my memory or my reasoning. The bones of my skull are still fragile, but knitting together well. Even my face has returned to pretty much how it looked before the night of 11 June. The only visible scar is the one across the top of my head. Most ways you look at it, my recovery is every bit the miracle that Auntie I prayed for.

When I look at some of the other patients here – men and women who are partially or completely paralysed, or have lost arms and legs – I know I've nothing to complain about. I can walk and I can run. And even though part of my brain has been cut away, I can talk and I can think. It's just the pain. The pain in my shoulder, the pain in my back and the pain in my head … The doctors tell me it will go, one day, but I wonder whether they are just saying that to give me hope. I don't think I'll ever get used to it.

CHAPTER 31

There's a place I go to in Headley Court where I try to make sense of everything that has happened, a little garden, surrounded by a high, carefully trimmed hedge, filled with roses that I can't smell. In the middle of the garden is a bench. I sit here during breaks in my schedule, thinking about the past and the future. I think about the things I used to build and wonder whether I'll ever be able to build anything again. I think about Grenada and England and the army and wonder which of them is now my home. I think about life outside the army, and wonder where my future lies.

I think about Gran.

Little by little, as the summer drifts into autumn, I feel my strength returning. The pain in my head begins to ease too. Is this because I'm getting better or because I'm getting used to it? I don't know. The doctors don't really know either. With an injury like mine, a lot is down to guesswork.

One warm October morning I'm sitting in the garden, the sun on my face, when my mobile rings. It's a crackly line.

'That you?'

'Sammy!'

I feel a rush of excitement that I haven't felt for months. '

'The battalion's back. We got back this mornin'. How you doing, man?'

'I'm good,' I tell him. 'What's it like to be back?'

We talk for half an hour. He asks when I'm next coming back to Tidworth and I tell him that it doesn't figure in my plans any more.

'What about you?' I say. 'What are your plans?'

Sammy tells me the battalion is due a whole load of leave, then it's Christmas, then it's on the move again – to Paderborn in Germany, until March 2006, when it's due to head back to Iraq for another tour of duty.

I know one thing for sure, I tell him. I won't be going with them. The doctors and physiotherapists at Headley Court say that my wounds have made me unfit for military service. I'll be discharged from the army as soon as my course of treatment is over.

*

One spring morning, shortly after a hydrotherapy session, I get a call from Colonel Maer. The Ministry of Defence has arranged for some of the guys in the battalion who fought in Iraq to be interviewed by the media. Apparently I'm one of the ones they want to speak to. The CO also wants to talk about my future. Accommodation is being arranged in

London. Some of my mates will be there too. A car comes to pick me up from Headley Court and I rendezvous with Colonel Maer in the lobby of his hotel. He steers me into a small conference room, where we chat about my injuries, and my recovery. The CO looks at his watch. Almost immediately there's a knock on the door and Mr Deane walks into the room.

'Boss!' I say, jumping to my feet.

'Beharry ...' He grabs my hand warmly.

*

I glance over Mr Deane's shoulder. Sergeant Major Falconer is standing next to the CO. Broomstick is standing beside him. I step forward and shake his hand.

When we settle down, the CO tells us a little bit about what we can expect at the Ministry of Defence tomorrow. There are some awards to be made, some medals to be handed out later in the year, he says, and the MoD wants to make sure that the media have everything they need to start preparing their account of our deployment in Al Amarah.

'I've got to go over there now and prepare some of the groundwork,' he says, getting to his feet. 'But I'll be back later to give you an update.'

In the evening, when he returns from the MoD, the CO calls us into a seminar room on the ground floor of the hotel.

He says he has something to tell us. He stares at his feet for a moment, then looks at us.

'When I took over the battalion, I told you I'd be straight with you. That you'd always get the truth from me. Well, today, I'm afraid, I broke that rule.'

I don't know what the CO is talking about. When I look at Mr Deane, the CSM and Broomstick, I see they don't either.

'Around a week ago, I was told, under strict instructions not to tell a living soul, that the battalion would be in line to receive a number of awards for our contribution to Op Telic. Tomorrow, one day in advance of the announcement, the press is to be pre-briefed on those awards. I'm delighted to inform you that the battalion has done rather well. You, gentlemen, are all among those who are going to be honoured.' He looks at Mr Deane and Sergeant Major Falconer and says, 'Richard, Sergeant Major, you've both got MCs.' Mr Deane looks stunned. He stares at the floor and goes very quiet. 'Twice wounded and twice returned to battle,' the CO says. 'Quite outstanding, Richard. Well done.'

Falconer sits there, shaking his head. 'I'm thinking of the blokes, sir. They're the ones who deserve this, not me.'

'Your leadership and courage throughout Telic Four were exemplary,' the CO says. 'As far as I'm concerned, Sergeant Major, they've got it right. I'm proud of you. We all are.' The CO turns to Broomstick. 'The Conspicuous Gallantry Cross for you, Sergeant Broome. Second only to the Victoria Cross for bravery in the face of the enemy. You're one of only fifteen people to have been awarded the CGC since it was instituted in 1993.'

Broomstick almost falls off his chair.

'Me? Why me, sir?'

'I can think of any number of reasons,' the CO says. 'But the citation stresses your selfless courage in coming to Sergeant Llewellyn's rescue on 9 May.' There's a long pause, then the CO looks at me. 'Beharry,' he says, 'this one's rather special. They haven't handed one of these out for quite a while. It gives me the very deepest pleasure to tell you that you are going to receive the Victoria Cross.'

CHAPTER 32

Buckingham Palace, London, 27 April 2005

We're greeted by the Queen's equerry-in-waiting and led through the corridors to the ballroom. As soon as my family are settled one row from the front, I'm directed into a side room to be briefed on the ceremony. I'm the first in line to be decorated; around 150 others will follow. It all seems straightforward enough.

I wait in the wings for the band to strike up the National Anthem on the dot of eleven. Everybody rises as the Queen walks into the ballroom. Before I have time to get nervous, they sit again and my name is called out.

'Private Johnson Beharry, The Princesses of Wales' Royal Regiment. For his actions on 1 May and 11 June 2004 in saving the lives of his Warrior crew by dogged and determined perseverance when injured and under sustained enemy attack. The Victoria Cross.'

I keep walking until I'm standing a few short paces from Her Majesty. I look her in the eyes and the corner of her mouth twitches. Is it a smile? Do I smile back?

The Lord Chamberlain, standing to the Queen's right, begins to read my citation.

'Private Beharry carried out two individual acts of great heroism, by which he saved the lives of his comrades. Both were in direct face of the enemy, under intense fire, at great personal risk to himself, one leading to him sustaining very serious injuries. His valour is worthy of the highest recognition ...'

It takes almost fifteen minutes to read it out, by which time my shoulder and back are killing me. I step up to receive my medal. I bow and find myself half a pace away from the Queen. I have so much blood pounding in my ears that I miss the first thing she says to me. 'I'm sorry, Majesty?'

She leans forward and her face breaks into a big smile.

'You're a very special person,' she says, as she pins the medal on to my chest. 'It's been rather a long time since I've awarded one of these.'

AFTERWORD

Since 1856, 1355 VCs have been awarded – and eleven (not including mine) since the Second World War (six of them posthumously). The last surviving recipient was Lance Corporal Rambahadur Limbu of the 10th Gurkha Rifles for his action in Sarawak, Borneo, in November 1965. Lieutenant Colonel H. Jones and Sergeant Ian McKay, of the Parachute Regiment, received them posthumously during the Falklands War in 1982. Four VCs have been awarded to Australians – two of them posthumously – for actions during the Vietnam War. Fourteen VC holders, including me, are still alive.

Maybe I was brave, I don't know. At the time I was just doing the job. I didn't have time for other thoughts. As a wise person once said: Some days you the bug, some days you the windshield.

ACKNOWLEDGEMENTS

I'd like to give special thanks to Irene Beharry, who was here for me on day one and who is still here. Thank you, Irene – I love you. I'd also like to reiterate my thanks to Raymond, Gavin and Darren for helping me through some difficult moments. The same goes to my family and friends, named and unnamed, and to anyone else who hasn't been mentioned either here or directly in the text, but who played their part – my profound thanks and, where appropriate, apologies. I haven't forgotten you and you know that I never will.

A deep, deep debt of thanks goes to the officers and men of the 1st Battalion Princesses of Wales's Royal Regiment, especially the guys who served with me in Al Amarah in that sweltering summer of 2004. You know who you are – I certainly do. I will never forget you either.

Another deep debt of thanks goes to Mr Kay and Mr Evans at the Queen Elizabeth Neuroscience Centre and Pam Wells at Headley Court.

I would also like to express my lasting gratitude to all the doctors and medical staff in Kuwait, Birmingham, Headley Court and Woolwich who helped my recovery.

Further thanks go to Prime Minister Keith Mitchell, Senator Einstein Louison, Minister Clarice Modeste-Curwen and the government of Grenada, and to Captain Chris Wright, Colonel Frances Castle, Colonel Mike Ball, Richard Holmes and the Ministry of Defence, and to Didy Grahame of the VC & GC Association.

I am also indebted to Lieutenant Colonel Eric Wilson VC and all the other VC recipients who have shared the benefit of their advice and wisdom with me. It has meant, and continues to mean, so much.

USEFUL WORDS AND ABBREVIATIONS

AK47	– a type of rifle
calypso	– a style of music made popular in the Caribbean
casevac	– short for 'casualty-evacuation'
Chinook	– a type of helicopter used by the military
contact area	– location of confrontation with the enemy
galvanized	– ridged steel used for building
IED	– improvised explosive device
IRT	– immediate response team
klicks	– military slang for 'kilometres'
LOCSTAT	– 'location status'
machete	– a type of large knife, often used to cut away vegetation
manicou	– a type of possum

MoD	– the Ministry of Defence
mortar unit	– a type of short-range weapon
Muqtadar Al-Sadr	– an Iraqi leader; enemy of the Coalition forces
neutral turn	– a sharp turn performed when a vehicle is not in gear
NAAFI	– Navy, Army and Air Force Institute
noni tree	– a type of tropical tree with flowers and fruits all year round
nutmeg	– a type of spice, grown in the Caribbean
oildown	– a type of stew
ops room	– operations room
Op Telic	– the codename for UK military operations in Iraq from 2003 to 2011
platoon	– a military unit
recce	– short for 'reconnaissance'
RMP	– the Royal Military Police
RPG	– rocket-propelled grenade
rum	– a type of alcoholic drink made in the Caribbean
SA40	– a type of rifle

sandbagging	– building defensive walls with sand-filled bags
Saviour	– another way of describing Jesus, the Son of God in the Christian faith
standpipe	– an outdoor public tap